Jonathan Bygrave

STARTER

Total English

Workbook (with key)

PEARSON

Longman

Contents

1.1 Arrivals

Speaking

1 **a** Complete the conversations with words from the box.

> Welcome   too   Thank   I'm   ~~Nice~~
> name   Hi

1 **A:** Hello. I'm Ajala Kapoor.
  B: Hello. I'm Rick Lane. _Nice_ to meet you.
  A: Nice to meet you, _____ .

2 **A:** Hi, Mona.
  B: _____ , Andre.

3 **A:** Good morning.
  B: Good morning.
  A: _____ to Mercer Hotel.
  B: _____ you.

4 **A:** Hello. I'm Charles Reed. What's your _____ ?
  B: _____ Taku Suzuki.

b Match a conversation in Ex. 1a to a picture below.

A

Conversation ___

B

Conversation ___

C

Conversation ___

D

Conversation ___

Vocabulary | numbers 0–9

2 Complete the crossword.

Across →		Down ↓	
c	1	a	2
e	5	b	8
g	6	d	4
h	3	f	7
i	9		

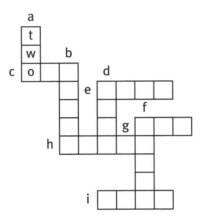

Listening

3 **1.1** Listen and write the room numbers.

1

2

3

4

5

6

Grammar | *I'm/you're*

4 Look at the information. Complete the conversations.

1

Linton HOTEL

NAME David Franks
ROOM 601

A: Hello. Welcome *to Linton Hotel*.
B: Thank you. *I'm David Franks*.
A: *You're in room 601*, Mr Franks.

2

GRANGE HOTEL

Name Susan Jacks
Room 329

A: Hello. Welcome _____ .
B: Thank you. _____ .
A: _____ , Ms Jacks.

3

OPERA HOTEL

Name Ricardo Mendoza
Room 540

A: Hello. Welcome _____ .
B: Thank you. _____ .
A: _____ , Mr Mendoza.

5 Correct the mistakes in the conversations.

1 A: Hello. (I) Svetlana Rochev.   *I'm*
   B: Hello, Ms Rochev.
2 A: Good morning, Mr Nakamura. You in room 922.
   B: Thank you.
3 A: Hello. Im Jin Chang.
   B: Im Farah Coleman.
4 A: I'm John Wilson.
   B: Hello, Mr Wilson. Youre in room 102.

Vocabulary | greetings

6 Write a conversation for each picture.

07.30
Henry: Good morning, Ms Sharapova.
Maria Sharapova: *Good morning, Henry.*
15.30
Henry: _____ , _____ .
Bob Geldof: _____ , _____ .
19.30
Henry: _____ , _____ .
Gwyneth Paltrow: _____ , _____ .
23.00
Henry: _____ , _____ .
Jamie Foxx: _____ , _____ .

7 Put the conversation into the correct order.

> I'm Polly Tiller   Nice to meet you   ~~Good morning~~
> I'm Evan Larson   Nice to meet you, too   Good morning

Evan: *Good morning*.
Polly: _____ .
Evan: _____ .
Polly: _____ .
Evan: _____ .
Polly: _____ .

Vocabulary | letters a–z

1 a Write the correct number for the vowel sound next to each letter.

	VOWEL SOUND	EXAMPLE
1	/eɪ/	<u>eigh</u>t
2	/ɪː/	thr<u>ee</u>
3	/e/	t<u>e</u>n
4	/aɪ/	f<u>i</u>ve
5	/eʊ/	zer<u>o</u>
6	/uː/	tw<u>o</u>
7	/ɑː/	<u>a</u>re

a *b* *c* *d*
_1_ _2_ _2_ _

e *f* *g* *h*
_ _ _ _

i *j* *k* *l*
_ _ _ _

m *n* *o* *p*
_ _ _ _

q *r* *s* *t*
_ _ _ _

u *v* *w* *x*
_ _ _ _

y *z*
_ _

b 🔊 **1.2** Listen and check.

Vocabulary | countries

2 a Correct the spelling and mark the stress.

1 Itily *Italy*
2 Polan _____
3 Mexica _____
4 Turkiy _____
5 Espain _____
6 Rusia _____
7 Argantina _____
8 Brasil _____

b Complete the puzzle to find the hidden country.

1
5
2
6
3
7
4

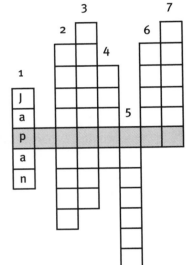

Grammar | he's/she's/it's

3 Write sentences with *he's*, *she's* or *it's*.

1 Sergio
He's Sergio.

2 Francesca

_____.

3 London
_____.

4 Amy
_____.

5 New York

_____.

6 Calvin

_____.

4 Write two sentences for each picture.

US

1   *He's from Brazil. He's in the US* .

the UK

2   She _____ .

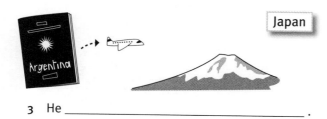

Japan

3   He _____ .

Australia

4   He _____ .

India

5   She _____ .

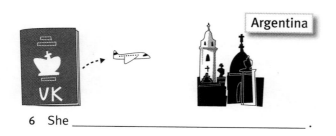

Argentina

6   She _____ .

Reading

5 Read the conversation and complete the details 1–3 below about the three people.

Candy:	Hello. I'm Candy Banks.
Paul:	Hello, Candy. I'm Paul Earle.
Candy:	Nice to meet you, Paul.
Paul:	Nice to meet you, too. Look, she's Marsha.
Candy:	Marsha?
Paul:	Yes. Marsha Rees. She's from Fort Lauderdale.
Candy:	In the UK?
Paul:	No. Fort Lauderdale is in Florida, in the US.
Candy:	Oh.
Receptionist:	Mr Earle?
Paul:	Yes.
Receptionist:	Good morning, Mr Earle. Welcome to Fortune Hotel.
Paul:	Thank you.
Receptionist:	You're in room eight nine one.
Paul:	OK. Thanks.
Receptionist:	And Ms Banks?
Candy:	Yes.
Receptionist:	Welcome to Fortune Hotel, Ms Banks. You're in room six one four.
Candy:	Thank you.

1

Name: _____
From: _____

2

Name: _____
Room: _____

3

Name: _____
Room: _____

Vocabulary | common phrases

1 **a** Write the complete words and phrases.

1 S__rry.

2 P__rd__n?

3 N__, th__nk y__ __.

4 N__c__ t__ m__ __t y__ __.

5 __xc__s__ m__.

6 Y__s, pl__ __s__.

b Match a phrase from Ex 1a to a picture below.

a

b

c

d

e

f

How to ... | introduce people

2 Complete the dialogues. Follow the example.

1 **Student A** = Nicole   **Student B** = Keith

You: *Nicole, this is Keith*.

Nicole: *Nice to meet you, Keith*.

Keith: *Nice to meet you too, Nicole*.

2 **Student A** = Colin   **Student B** = Laura

You: _____ .

Colin: _____ .

Laura: _____ .

3 **Student A** = Harry   **Student B** = Mary

You: _____ .

Harry: _____ .

Mary: _____ .

Grammar | *Where are you from?*

3 Put the words in the correct order.

Theo: is Ali. this Carol,

Carol, this is Ali .

Carol: meet to Nice you.

_____ .

Ali: meet to too. you, Nice

_____ .

Carol: from, Where Ali? are you

_____ ?

Ali: from UK. the I'm

_____ .

Carol: you are from Where the UK? in

_____ ?

Ali: from London. I'm

_____ .

4 Complete the conversations.

1 A: Where *are* you _____ in the US?

B: I'm from Chicago.

2 A: _____ _____ you from?

B: I'm from Tokyo in Japan.

3 A: Where are _____ _____ in Brazil?

B: I'm from Curitiba.

4 A: Where are _____ _____ ?

B: I'm _____ Australia.

5 A: _____ are you from in the UK?

B: I'm _____ Manchester.

6 A: Where _____ you _____ ?

B: _____ from Spain.

5 Write questions and answers.

1

You: _____ _____ _____ from in the Italy?
Isabella: _____ _____ Rome.

2

You: _____ _____ _____ _____ ?
Shah: _____ _____ India.

3

You: _____ _____ _____ _____ ?
Fabiana: _____ _____ Argentina.

4

You: _____ _____ _____ _____ in Mexico?
Gael: _____ _____ Guadalajara.

Listening

6 `1.3` Cover the tapescript and listen. Complete the details.

1 **Name:** Stan _____
   From: _____ (city)
   From: _____ (country)

2 **Name:** Nadine _____
   From: _____ (city)
   From: _____ (country)

3 **Name:** Chris _____
   From: _____ (city)
   From: _____ (country)

TAPESCRIPT

Stan: Hello.
Nadine: Hello.
Stan: I'm Stan Allman. What's your name?
Nadine: I'm Nadine Strong.
Stan: Nice to meet you, Nadine.
Nadine: Nice to meet you too, Stan.
Stan: This is Chris, Chris Hall.
Chris: Hello.
Nadine: Hello.
Stan: Where are you from, Nadine?
Nadine: Pardon?
Stan: Where are you from?
Nadine: Oh. I'm from the US.
Stan: Oh really? Where are you from in the US?
Nadine: Dallas. It's in Texas.
Stan: Chris is from America.
Chris: No – I'm from Canada!
Stan: Oh, yes. Sorry.
Nadine: Where are you from in Canada, Chris?
Chris: Victoria. It's in British Colombia.
Nadine: Where are you from, Stan. Canada, too?
Stan: No – I'm from Brighton in the UK.
Nadine: Oh, OK. My mother is from the UK.

Vocabulary | family members

1 Look at the photo. How are the people related?

Sharon   Jack   Ozzy   Kelly

1 Ozzy – Jack = *father* – *son*
2 Ozzy – Sharon = _____ – _____
3 Kelly – Jack = _____ – _____
4 Sharon – Kelly = _____ – _____
5 Jack – Sharon = _____ – _____
6 Kelly – Ozzy = _____ – _____

Vocabulary | my life

2 Write the words in the grid. Find the secret word.

9 Park Road
London
NW14 9IU

Back Forward Stop Refresh
Address: @ http://www.google.com

Tom Green

Tom Green

Crossword:
1 p h o n e

Numbers 10–99

3 Match the numbers 1–10 to a–j.

1 fifty-one _51_   a) 93
2 forty-eight   b) 15
3 eleven   c) **73**
4 sixteen   d) *48*
5 ninety-three   e) 11
6 seventy-three   f) ~~51~~
7 fifteen   g) *84*
8 sixty   h) **39**
9 eighty-four   i) **60**
10 thirty-nine   j) **16**

4 Write the next two numbers in the sequences.

1 two four eight sixteen *thirty-two* *sixty-four*

2 eleven twenty-two thirty-three forty-four
   _____ _____

3 ninety eighty seventy sixty _____
   _____

4 sixteen fifteen fourteen thirteen _____
   _____

5 forty-nine fifty-six sixty-three seventy
   _____ _____

6 twenty-seven thirty-six forty-five _____
   _____

7 sixteen twenty-five thirty-six forty-nine
   _____ _____

8 ninety ten eighty twenty _____
   _____

Grammar | Who ...?; my

5 Look at the family tree and complete the conversation.

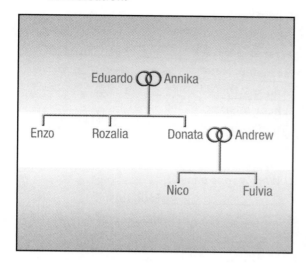

Ivan:	Nice photo!
Donata:	Thank you! It's a photo of my family.
Ivan:	(1) *Who's* he?
Donata:	He's my (2) _____ , Andrew. He's from the US.
Ivan:	New York?
Donata:	No, Los Angeles.
Ivan:	And who's (3) _____ ?
Donata:	She's Rozalia. She's (4) _____ sister. She's in Italy. And he's my (5) _____ , Eduardo. He's in Italy, too.
Ivan:	(6) _____ he?
Donata:	He's Nico. He's my (7) _____ . And she's Fulvia, (8) _____ daughter.
Ivan:	(9) _____ she?
Donata:	She's my (10) _____ , Annika. She's from Germany.
Ivan:	An international family! Who's (11) _____ ?
Donata:	(12) _____ Enzo, my brother.

6 **2.1** Cover the tapescript below and listen. Write the age of each person in the family tree.

TAPESCRIPT

Donata: I'm forty-one. My brother is twenty-nine and my sister is thirty-six. My husband is forty-four. My son is twelve and my daughter is eight. My mother is sixty-seven and my father is seventy-two.

Reading

7 Read the text and complete the details about the people.

Who is Devandra?
Devandra Branley is my friend. He's from San Diego in the US. He's thirty-five years old.

Who is Darren?
Darren is my father – Darren Southgate. He's fifty-seven. He's from Edinburgh in Scotland.

Who is Beverley?
Beverley Wolcott is my friend, too. She's from Dominica in the Caribbean. She's thirty-seven years old.

Who is Pauline?
Pauline Southgate is my mother. She's from York in the UK. She's sixty years old.

Who are you?
I'm David. I'm from Manchester in the UK. I'm twenty-nine.

NAME: Darren Southgate
AGE: _____
FROM: _____ in _____
RELATIONSHIP TO DAVID: father

NAME: _____ _____
AGE: 35 years old
FROM: _____ in _____
RELATIONSHIP TO DAVID: _____

NAME: _____ _____
AGE: _____
FROM: _____ in _____
RELATIONSHIP TO DAVID: friend

NAME: _____ Southgate
AGE: _____
FROM: _____ in _____
RELATIONSHIP TO DAVID: mother

Vocabulary | expressions

1 Match a word in the box to a picture 1–5 below.

> bad   great   ~~good~~   awful   OK

1. 😊   *good*
2. 😟😟   _____
3. 😊😊   _____
4. 😐   _____
5. 😞   _____

2 Write a sentence for each singer. Use a word from Ex. 1.

1 *She's good.*

2 _____ .

3 _____ .

4 _____ .

5 _____ .

Grammar | What's your ...?

3 Look at the profile and complete the questions and answers.

> **First name:** Fadil
> **Surname:** Husni
> **Address:** 93 Al Orouba Street, Cairo
> **Phone number:** 02366 48381
> **Mobile phone number:** 08112 828344

1 *What's your* name?
   _____ _____ Fadil Husni.
2 _____ _____ _____ ?
   _____ 93 Al Orouba Street, Cairo.
3 _____ _____ _____ _____ ?
   _____ 02366 48381.
4 _____ _____ _____ _____
   _____ ?
   _____ 08112 828344.

4 Write questions with *Who, What, Where* or *How*.

1 *Who's she*?
   She's my friend.
2 _____ ?
   I'm fifty-five.
3 _____ ?
   Jane Sutter.
4 _____ ?
   It's 01323 594 392.
5 _____ ?
   He's nineteen.
6 _____ ?
   Parson. P – A – R – S – O –N.
7 _____ ?
   I'm from Colchester in the UK.
8 _____ ?
   75 Attley Street, Cambridge.
9 _____ ?
   Preston is my brother.
10 _____ ?
   She's from China.

5 There are five mistakes in each conversation. Correct the mistakes.

Conversation A

Receptionist: Good morning. Welcome ~~the~~ to the Hatson Hotel.

Olivia: Thank you.

Receptionist: What your name, please?

Olivia: I Olivia Dukakis.

Receptionist: How you spell Dukakis?

Olivia: D – U – K – A – K – I – S.

Receptionist: Thank you, Ms Dukakis. You in room 815.

Conversation B

Mr Crowley: Hello.

Ricky: Hello.

Mr Crowley: What's name, please?

Ricky: Ricky Morley.

Mr Crowley: How do you spell, please?

Ricky: Morley. M – O – R – L – E – Y.

Mr Crowley: What your address, Ricky?

Ricky: Flat 3, 81 Tavistock Street, Wimbledon.

Mr Crowley: What do you spell Tavistock?

Ricky: T – A – V – I – S – T – O – C – K.

Mr Crowley: And what's your phone?

Ricky: 020 8741 3841.

Writing

7 Write the text messages in full.

1 *Are you from Poland?*

2 _____

3 _____

4 _____

5 _____

Listening

6 [2.2] Cover the tapescript below and listen. Complete the details.

First name: _____

Surname: _____

Address: _____

_____

Phone number: _____

TAPESCRIPT

Woman: What's your name, please?

Man: I'm Brett Ellis.

Woman: How do you spell that?

Man: Brett. B – R – E – T – T. Ellis. E – L – L – I – S.

Woman: Thank you. What's your address?

Man: 33 Peel Street, Newcastle.

Woman: How do you spell that, please?

Man: Peel Street. P – E – E – L. Newcastle. N – E – W – C – A – S – T – L – E.

Woman: And what's your phone number?

Man: Double oh, Double four, one – nine – one, two – oh – two, one – four – nine.

Vocabulary | jobs

1   Complete the words to spell the jobs.

1   m <u>a</u> n <u>a</u> g <u>e</u> r
2   t _ _ c h _ r
3   s t _ d _ n t
4   _ c c _ _ n t _ n t
5   s _ l _ s   _ s s _ s t _ n t
6   p _ l _ c _   _ f f _ c _ r

7   d _ c t _ r
8   _ r t _ s t
9   _ n g _ n _ _ r
10 _ c t _ r

2   Complete the crossword.

Down

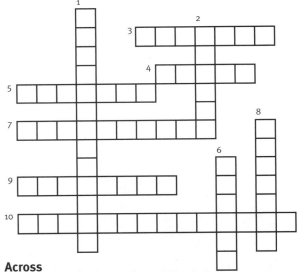

Across

Grammar 1 | a/an

3   Write sentences about each picture in Ex. 2. Use *a/an*.

1   *He's a police officer*.
2   _____ .
3   _____ .
4   _____ .
5   _____ .
6   _____ .
7   _____ .
8   _____ .
9   _____ .
10 _____ .

Information

4   Match a word or phrase 1–6 to the answer a–f.

1 name	a) julia.mann@mail.net
2 job	b) Julia Mann
3 address	c) engineer
4 age	d) 023 896537
5 email address	e) 34
6 phone number	f) 12 King Street, London

Grammar 2 | his/her

5   Circle the correct word.

This is Michael Douglas.
(1) (He's)/His an actor.
(2) He's/His from the US.
(3) He's/His sixty-two years old. (4) He's/His wife is Catherine Zeta Jones.
(5) She's/Her thirty-seven years old. (6) She's/Her an actor, too.

This is Michelle Douglas.
(7) She's/Her a sales assistant. (8) She's/Her from the UK. (9) She's/Her twenty-six years old.
(10) She's/Her husband is David Douglas. (11) He's/His twenty-seven years old.
(12) He's/His a doctor.

6 Complete the questions and answe

A: What's (1) *his* name?

B: (2) _____ name's Kemal Atlan.

A: Where's (3) _____ from?

B: (4) _____ from Turkey.

A: How old is (5) _____ ?

B: (6) _____ fifty-five.

A: What's (7) _____ job?

B: (8) _____ a manager.

A: What's (9) _____ email address?

B: (10) _____ kemal@freemail.com.

A: What's (11) _____ name?

B: (12) _____ name's Alva Braun.

A: Where's (13) _____ from?

B: (14) _____ from Vienna in Austria.

A: How old is (15) _____ ?

B: (16) _____ forty years old.

A: What's (17) _____ job?

B: (18) _____ an engineer.

A: What's (19) _____ mobile phone number?

B: (20) _____ 07932 787221.

Vocabulary | favourites

8 Write questions with *What's/Who's your favourite ...?* and a word from the box.

> book   restaurant   ~~city~~   CD
> singer   actor   film

1 *What's your favourite city*?
   Las Vegas.

2 _____ ?
   Gerrard's Bistro in Paris.

3 _____ ?
   Aretha Franklin.

4 _____ ?
   Toy Story 2.

5 _____ ?
   The Da Vinci Code by Dan Brown.

6 _____ ?
   Forty Licks by the The Rolling Stones.

7 _____ ?
   Robert de Niro.

Reading

7 Complete the family tree with the name, age and job of each person.

The Wallace family

He's Sam Wallace. His sister is Marie. He's forty-five years old and he's an engineer. His wife is Monica.

She's Patricia Wallace. Her son is Sam. She's sixty-eight years old and she's a teacher.

She's Debbie Wallace. Her mother is Monica. She's eleven years old and she's a student.

He's Derek Wallace. His wife is Patricia and his daughter is Marie. He's sixty-five years old and he's a doctor.

He's Malcolm Wallace. He's twelve years old and he's a student. His father is Sam and his mother is Monica.

She's Monica Wallace. Her husband is Sam. She's forty-four years old and she's an accountant.

She's Marie Wallace. Her brother is Sam. She's thirty-eight years old and she's a manager.

Name: _____
Age: _____
Job: _____

Name: _____
Age: _____
Job: _____

Name: _____
Age: _____
Job: _____

Name: *Sam*
Age: *45*
Job: *engineer*

Name: _____
Age: _____
Job: _____

Name: _____
Age: _____
Job: _____

Name: _____
Age: _____
Job: _____

Review and consolidation units 1-2

Grammar Verb *to be* with *I, you, he, she, it*

1 Circle the correct word.

1 He *am/is/are* from Russia.
2 I *am/is/are* a student.
3 It *am/is/are* my car.
4 You *am/is/are* a good singer.
5 I *am/is/are* Mike.
6 Catherine *am/is/are* an accountant.
7 You *am/is/are* my friend.
8 She *am/is/are* my manager.
9 I *am/is/are* from the UK.
10 Tom *am/is/are* in Istanbul.

2 Write the sentences with contractions.

1 She is Mrs Grant.
   She's Mrs Grant.
2 It is a great CD.
   _____ .
3 You are my favourite teacher.
   _____ .
4 I am Mr Brown.
   _____ .
5 He is from New York.
   _____ .
6 Colette is a student.
   _____ .
7 Peter is in China.
   _____ .
8 You are 21 years old.
   _____ .
9 I am in Hotel Fernando.
   _____ .
10 It is my favourite film.
   _____ .

my, your, his, her

3 Write *my*, *your*, *his*, *her* or *its* in the gaps.

1 He's my father. *His* name is Dave.
2 This is Moscow. _____ the capital of Russia.
3 I'm Yves. _____ surname is Connor.
4 Hello. What's _____ name?
5 Jasmine is my friend. _____ email address is jasmine@xpressmail.net.
6 _____ name is Julie. Nice to meet you.
7 I'm in an awful hotel. _____ name is Hotel Riviera.
8 Miguel is an artist. _____ favourite film is *The Godfather*.
9 You're my friend. _____ father is my friend, too.
10 Rachel is in India. _____ mobile phone number is 00 44 7823 23082.

Where, Who, What, How

4 Match a question 1–10 to an answer a–j.

1 Where are you from?
2 How old are you?
3 Who is she?
4 What is it?
5 Who are you?
6 Where is Fuerte Ventura?
7 How old is he?
8 What is his name?
9 What's your favourite film?
10 Who's he?

a) It's in Spain.
b) She's my manager.
c) David.
d) It's a camera.
e) I'm forty-nine.
f) He's my father.
g) He's nineteen.
h) I'm Martin Creek.
i) *Superman II*.
j) Lublin in Poland.

a/an

5 Complete each sentence with *a*, *an* or nothing (–).

1 Natalie is in _–_ India.
2 Jamie is _a_ sales assistant.
3 Emma is _____ actor.
4 What's your _____ email address?
5 It's _____ good film.
6 Madrid is _____ great city.
7 She's from _____ Russia.
8 He's my _____ brother.
9 She's _____ accountant.
10 Who's your favourite _____ singer?

Numbers 0–99

6 Match a number 1–10 to a number a–j.

1 84   a) nineteen
2 17   b) seven
3 11   c) fifteen
4 7   d) eleven
5 50   e) eighty-four
6 68   f) seventeen
7 19   g) twenty-three
8 70   h) fifty
9 23   i) seventy
10 15   j) sixty-eight

7 Write the numbers in full.

1 25 _twenty-five_
2 18 _____
3 50 _____
4 31 _____
5 12 _____
6 99 _____
7 44 _____
8 14 _____
9 82 _____
10 67 _____

Vocabulary

8 Tick ✓ the correct box.

	numbers	jobs	adjectives	family
1 manager	☐	✓	☐	☐
2 brother	☐	☐	☐	☐
3 awful	☐	☐	☐	☐
4 good	☐	☐	☐	☐
5 eighty	☐	☐	☐	☐
6 accountant	☐	☐	☐	☐
7 eleven	☐	☐	☐	☐
8 son	☐	☐	☐	☐
9 bad	☐	☐	☐	☐
10 engineer	☐	☐	☐	☐
11 fifty	☐	☐	☐	☐
12 wife	☐	☐	☐	☐

9 Complete the sentences below with the words in the box.

> sixty   passport   favourite   address   officer
> assistant   Excuse   Nice   ~~singer~~   website

1 My favourite _singer_ is Billie Holiday.
2 My _____ is 19 Brancaster Lane, Selsdon.
3 _____ me. Are you Derek?
4 She's a great sales _____ .
5 The photo in my _____ is very old.
6 Youtube.com is a great _____ .
7 My mother is _____ years old.
8 Is this your _____ CD?
9 _____ to meet you, too.
10 She's a police _____ .

3.1 Travel

Vocabulary | tourist attractions

1 Find eight tourist attractions in the grid.

c	m	u	s	e	u	m	d	o
a	f	m	r	p	e	j	m	j
s	e	a	l	a	k	e	o	s
t	h	r	t	l	e	l	u	y
l	j	k	y	a	d	r	n	t
e	l	e	u	c	n	a	t	q
c	a	t	h	e	d	r	a	l
o	p	w	r	a	q	b	i	c
g	a	l	l	e	r	y	n	z

1 _castle_   5 ma_____
2 mo_____   6 g_____
3 c_____   7 p_____
4 mu_____   8 l_____

2 Match a word 1–8 from Ex.1 to a picture a–h below.

cathedral   _____

_____   _____

_____   _____

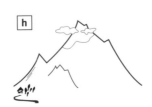

_____   _____

Vocabulary | adjectives

3 Put the words in the box into three pairs.

old   ugly   modern   small   beautiful   big

1 _____ – _____
2 _____ – _____
3 _____ – _____

4 Choose two adjectives from Ex. 3 for each picture.

A

B

C

E

D

F

A The car is _old_ and _beautiful_.
B The camera is _____ and _____ .
C The dinosaur is _____ and _____ .
D The fish is _____ and _____ .
E The mobile phone is _____ and _____ .
F The television is _____ and _____ .

Grammar | the verb *to be* with *we* and *they*; *our* and *their*

5 Circle the correct word.

1 My name is Kelly and his name is Larry. (We're)/ *Our* from Liverpool in the UK.

2 *They're/Their* daughter is Lucy.

3 Richard and Julia are teachers. *They're/Their* my friends.

4 Carla is my sister. *We're/Our* mother is from Slovakia.

5 Ulrika and Sebastian are in Sofia in Bulgaria. *They're/Their* in a hotel.

6 *We're/Our* car is very old.

7 What's *they're/their* email address?

8 Julian is a singer but *we're/our* actors.

6 Complete the email with *we're, they're, our* or *their*.

From: rebeccaclark55@gmail.com
To: tomandsusan.clark@yahoo.co.uk
Subject: We're in Recife!

Hi Mum and Dad,
How are you? Sarah and I are fine. (1) *We're* in Recife in Brazil. (2) _____ hotel is great. (3) _____ in room 1111!
Belinda and Cipriano are in Recife too. (4) _____ from São Paolo. They're (5) _____ friends.
The attachment is a photo of Belinda, Cipriano and Carlita in (6) _____ house in São Paolo. It's big! Carlita is (7) _____ daughter. She's beautiful.
Love
Roman

7 Complete the sentences with *we're, they're, our* or *their*.

Jones 42   Watson 38

1 Mr Watson: *Their* car is old. _____ car is modern.

2 Mr Jones: _____ a big family. _____ a small family.

3 Mrs Watson: _____ surname is Jones. _____ surname is Watson.

4 Mrs Jones: _____ forty-two. _____ thirty-eight.

5 Mrs Watson: _____ son is Casper. _____ sons are Wesley and Gary.

Writing

8 Put the sections of the email into the correct order.

a The attachment is my sister and me in Hotel Elise.

b See you soon!

c From: lomox@patermail.com
To: josephine29@qwertymail.com
Subject: our holiday!

d Lola

e Thanks for your email. We're on holiday in Nice in France. Our hotel is Hotel Elise. It's very small but it's great and Nice is beautiful.

f Hi Josephine

1 _c_   2 ___   3 ___
4 ___   5 ___   6 ___

Vocabulary | holiday things

1 Complete the words. Match a word/phrase to a picture.

Words	Photo
1 a _c a m e r a_	_D_
2 a t _ _ _	_
3 a b _ _ _ _ _ _ c _	_
4 a _ _ _ _ _ of _ r _ _ _ _ _ _ s	_
5 a _ o o _	_
6 a s _ _ r _	_
7 a _ _ _ _ _ of s _ _ _ _ _	_
8 a _ u _ t _ _ _ _ e	_
9 a m _ _	_
10 an _ _ 3 p _ _ _ _ _ _	_

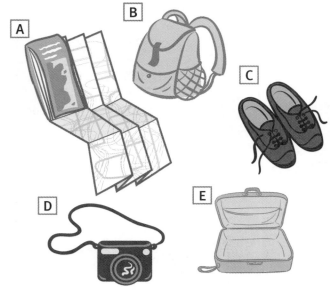

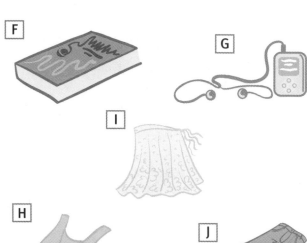

How to ... | make regular plurals

2   **a**   What's in the picture?

a	_Two CDs_.	f	_____
b	_____	g	_____
c	_____	h	_____
d	_____	i	_____
e	_____	j	_____

b   Write /s/, /z/ or /ɪz/ next to each plural noun in Ex. 2a.

3   Make the <u>underlined</u> words in the sentences plural.

1   <u>My</u> <u>camera</u> <u>is</u> in the suitcase.
    Our cameras are in the suitcase.

2   He's an <u>accountant</u>.
    They're accountants.

3   Where <u>is</u> <u>my</u> <u>backpack</u>?
    _____ ?

4   Who <u>is</u> your favourite <u>singer</u>?
    _____ ?

5   <u>Her</u> <u>map</u> <u>is</u> awful.
    _____ .

6   <u>It's</u> a great MP3 <u>player</u>.
    _____ .

7   <u>My</u> favourite <u>pair</u> of shoes <u>is</u> very old.
    _____ .

8   How old <u>is</u> <u>her</u> <u>daughter</u>?
    _____ ?

Grammar | the verb *to be*: negative

4 Write negative sentences with the verb *to be*.

1 He/my brother
He isn't my brother.

2 You/21 years old
_____.

3 It/my camera
_____.

4 Ronnie and Nicky/friends
_____.

5 London/my favourite city
_____.

6 We/students
_____.

7 I/a good actor
_____.

8 Simone/from Italy
_____.

9 Will and I/her teachers
_____.

10 I/very old
_____.

5 Correct the sentences.

1 A: I'm a teacher. (student)
B: *You're not a teacher*.
You're a student.

2 A: It's a skirt. (pair of trousers)
B: _____.
_____.

3 A: We're from the US. (the UK)
B: _____.
_____.

4 A: Vienna is my favourite country. (city)
B: _____.
_____.

5 A: He's my sister. (brother)
B: _____.
_____.

6 A: I'm fifteen. (fifty)
B: _____.
_____.

7 A: They're open today. (closed)
B: _____.
_____.

8 A: She's an accountant. (engineer)
B: _____.
_____.

Listening

6 **3.1** Cover the tapescript below and listen. Write true (T) or false (F) next to the sentences below.

1 The teacher is Peter Kuff.   *F*
2 Celia Cruz is the sister of Penelope Cruz.
3 Penelope Cruz is from Valencia in Spain.
4 Celia Cruz is from Valencia in Spain.
5 Raymond Petit is the brother of Catherine Petit.
6 Catherine and Raymond are from Marseilles in France.
7 Raymond is twenty-nine years old.
8 Catherine is twenty-four years old.
9 The teacher is forty-six years old.

TAPESCRIPT

Teacher: Good morning everyone. Where's the register. Ah, here it is. Three new students today! Who is Celia Cruz?

Celia: I am.

Teacher: Welcome to our English class, Celia. I'm Peter Keef: K – double E – F. So, you're from Italy.

Celia: No, I'm not. I'm from Spain.

Teacher: Ah. Penelope Cruz is from Spain. She's your sister!

Celia: No, no, she's not my sister. She's from Madrid and I'm not from Madrid. I'm from Valencia.

Teacher: Oh, OK. And who are Raymond Petit and Catherine Petit?

Raymond: We are.

Teacher: You're brother and sister.

Catherine: No, we aren't. Raymond is my husband.

Raymond: ... and Catherine is my wife.

Teacher: Wow! OK. You're married. Great. You're very young. How old are you? Twenty-three, twenty-four?

Raymond: No, no. I'm twenty-nine and Catherine is twenty-eight.

Teacher: Oh, OK. Where are you from?

Catherine: We're from Marseilles in France.

Raymond: And how old are you, Mr Keef? forty-five, forty-six?

Teacher: No! I'm forty-one.

7 Correct the false sentences in Ex. 6.

1 *The teacher is Peter Keef.*

Vocabulary | days of the week

1 Complete the days of the week. Then put them in order.

W _ _ n _ _ day
Th _ _ _ day
F _ _ day
M _ _ day
S _ t _ _ day
T _ _ _ day
S _ _ day

How to ... | use *here* and *there*

2 Choose the correct sentence for each picture.

a The cathedral is here.
b The cathedral is there.

a Here's your mobile phone.
b There's your mobile phone.

a Here's the gallery.
b There's the gallery.

a Here are your shoes.
b There are your shoes.

Grammar | lYes/No questions with *to be*

3 Complete the conversations then match them to a picture A–C below.

Conversation 1

A: Excuse me.
B: Yes?
A: (1) *Are* you from this town?
B: Yes, we (2) _____ .
A: Oh, good. (3) _____ the cathedral near here?
B: Yes, (4) _____ is. It's over there.
A: Thank you.

Conversation 2

A: (5) _____ the cinema big?
B: Yes, it (6) _____ , madam. (7) _____ very big.
A: And (8) _____ the film good?
B: It's very good. (9) _____ they your sons?
A: Yes, they (10) _____ .
B: (11) _____ (12) _____ over 11 years old.
A: No, they (13) _____ . They're 10 years old.
B: Sorry madam. The film is for children over 11 only.

Conversation 3

A: Hello, sir. (14) _____ this your backpack?
B: (15) _____ , it is.
A: And (16) _____ (17) _____ your suitcases?
B: Yes, (18) _____ (19) _____ .
A: What's your room number, sir?
B: It room 311.
A: OK. Thank you, sir.

4 Write questions with the adjectives in **bold**.

1 A: She's a singer.
  B: *Is she a good singer*? **good**
  A: Yes, she is.

2 A: It's a museum.
  B: _____? **big**
  A: No, it isn't.

3 A: He's a friend.
  B: _____? **new**
  A: No, he isn't.

4 A: They're lakes.
  B: _____? **beautiful**
  A: Yes, they are.

5 A: I'm an actor.
  B: _____? **good**
  A: Yes, I am.

6 A: They're cities.
  B: _____? **small**
  A: No, they aren't.

5 Complete the conversation.

MODERN TATE

What: a gallery
Open: Monday–Sunday
Where: London
Entrance: Free

A: Good morning. Can I help you?
B: (1) Yes. Is the Tate Modern _____ today?
A: (2) _____ , _____ _____ .
B: (3) Good. _____ _____ a museum?
A: (4) _____ , _____ _____ . It's a gallery.
B: (5) _____ _____ free?
A: (6) _____ , _____ _____ .
B: (7) _____ _____ near here?
A: (8) Yes, _____ _____ . Here's a map. We're here and the Tate Modern is there.
B: Great. Thank you. Goodbye.
A: Goodbye.

Reading

6 Read the text and match a text to a picture.

Lake Baikal is a beautiful lake in Siberia, Russia. It is near Irkutsk and it is very, very big. It is about 30 million years old.

The New Museum of Contemporary Art is in New York in the US. It is not old (about 30 years old) but it is great. It is open from Tuesday to Sunday. Entrance is $6.

'Dracula's Castle' is really Bran Castle. It's in the Carpathian Mountains in Romania. It is near Brasov and it is open from Tuesday to Sunday. It is about 800 years old. Entrance is about €2.

7 Read the text again and answer the questions.

Lake Baikal

1 Is Lake Baikal in Russia? *Yes, it is*.
2 Is it near Siberia? *No, it isn't. It's in Siberia*.
3 Is it small? _____
4 Is it old? _____

The New Museum of Contemporary Art

5 Is it in the UK? _____
6 Is it old? _____
7 Is it closed on Mondays? _____
8 Is it free? _____

Bran Castle

9 Is Bran Castle in Romania? _____
10 Is it near Bucharest? _____
11 Is it open on Mondays? _____
12 Is it free? _____

4.1 In town

Vocabulary | places in town

1 Complete the crossword to spell the name of a famous UK city.

 1   2

 3   4

UK city

1	m	a	r	k	e	t

2

3

4

5

6

7

8

9

10

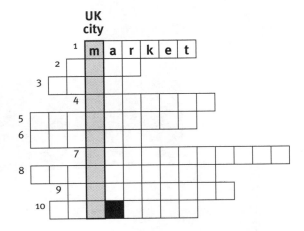 5   6

 7   8

 9   10

Vocabulary | food and drink

2 Complete the receipts for the trays of food.

1

CAFE CULTURE RECEIPT
LONDON
✱✱CUSTOMER COPY✱✱

a Chicken sandwich.........£2.99
b _____...........£1.09
c _____..............0.99

TOTAL..........................£5.07

2

PAULO'S CAFE RECEIPT
LISBON
✱✱CUSTOMER COPY✱✱

a _____..............€0.99
b _____..............€1.35
c _____..............€0.70

TOTAL......................€3.04

3

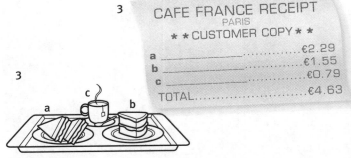

CAFE FRANCE RECEIPT
PARIS
✱✱CUSTOMER COPY✱✱

a _____..............€2.29
b _____..............€1.55
c _____..............€0.79

TOTAL..........................€4.63

Grammar | *Can I have ...?*

3 Complete the conversations with a word in each gap.

1 **A:** Hello. Can I (1) *help* you?

B: Can I have (2) _____ piece of cake and a mineral water, please?

A: Certainly. Anything else?

B: Yes. Can I have (3) _____ espresso, please?

A: Of course.

2 **A:** Hello. (4) _____ I help you?

B: Yes. Can I (5) _____ an espresso, a mineral water and a chicken salad, please?

A: Certainly. Anything else?

B: No, (6) _____ you.

3 **A:** Good morning.

B: Good morning. Can I have (7) _____ cheese sandwich and a piece of cake, please?

A: Sure. Anything (8) _____ ?

B: Yes. Can I have a cup of tea, (9) _____ ?

A: Certainly.

Vocabulary | prices

4 **a** Correct the mistakes.

1 (€1.90) That one euro ninety, please.
That's one euro ninety, please.

2 ($2.45) That's two dollar forty-five, please.
_____ .

3 (€0.50) That's fifty pence, please.
_____ .

4 (£6.29) That's six euros twenty-nine, please.
_____ .

5 (€3.60) That's three euro sixty cents, please.
_____ .

6 ($0.99) That's ninety-nine dollars, please.
_____ .

7 (€11.49) That's eleven forty-nine euros, please.
_____ .

8 (£0.80) That's eighty pounds, please.
_____ .

b Look at the pictures. Complete the sentences.

1 The CDs *are nine pounds eighty-nine*.
2 The pair of shoes _____ .
3 The camera _____ .
4 The backpack _____ .
5 The books _____ .
6 The mobile phone _____ .

Listening

5  Cover the tapescript and listen. Complete the menu board below.

> **TAPESCRIPT**
> **A:** Good afternoon. Can I help you?
> **B:** Yes. Can I have a chicken sandwich and a mineral water, please?
> **A:** Sure. Anything else?
> **B:** Yes, please. An orange juice.
> **A:** OK, the chicken sandwich is two pounds fifty and the mineral water is ninety pence. The orange juice is £1.20, so that's four sixty, please.
>
> **A:** Morning.
> **B:** Morning.
> **A:** What can I get you?
> **B:** Can I have an espresso, an iced coffee and a green salad, please? To take away.
> **A:** Sure. Anything else?
> **B:** No, thank you.
> **A:** OK, one espresso: that's one pound forty. One iced coffee: that's one pound ninety-five. And one green salad: that's three pounds and ten pence. So altogether that's six forty-five.
> **B:** Here you are.
> **A:** Great. Thanks.

∽ MENU ∽

FOOD
Chicken sandwich   £2.50
Green salad   _____

DRINKS
Orange juice   _____
Mineral water   _____

COFFEE
Espresso   _____
Iced coffee   _____

Vocabulary | clothes and colours

1 Find eight colours in the word square.

B	K	B	R	E	D
R	B	L	U	E	Y
O	R	A	N	G	E
W	P	C	D	R	L
N	Q	K	F	E	L
W	H	I	T	E	O
D	E	O	R	N	W

1 *b r o w n*   5 b _ _ _
2 w _ _ _ _   6 b l _ _ _
3 o _ _ _ _ _ _   7 y _ _ _ _ _
4 g _ _ _ _   8 r _ _

2 Look at the flags. What colours should they be?

1 Japan

It's red and white.

5 the UK
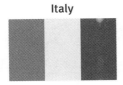
_____

2 Italy

_____

6 Spain
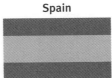
_____

3 Argentina

_____

7 Poland

_____

4 Germany

_____

8 Brazil

_____

3 Look at the picture. Write the items of clothing below.

1 *a hat*   5 _____
2 _____   6 _____
3 _____   7 _____
4 _____   8 _____

Grammar | *this, that, these, those*

4 Put the words into the correct order to make a sentence.

1 are white These nice. shirts
These white shirts are nice.

2 white €24. bag That is
_____ .

3 suitcase? your Is this
_____ ?

4 those Are new? tops
_____ ?

5 closed shops today. are These
_____ .

6 Clive. This my is brother,
_____ .

7 are Those beautiful. bags
_____ .

8 How coat? much that is
_____ ?

5 Look at the picture. Circle the correct word.

1 *this*/that/these/those bags (€5.99)
2 *this/that/these/those* shirts (€10.99)
3 *this/that/these/those* T-shirts (€4.99)
4 *this/that/these/those* tops (€15.99)
5 *this/that/these/those* hat (€4.50)
6 *this/that/these/those* coats (€77.99)
7 *this/that/these/those* skirts (€22.99)
8 *this/that/these/those* pairs of trousers (€18.59)

How to ... | talk about prices

6 Look at the picture in Ex. 5 again. Write the questions.

1 A: *How much are those shirts*?
   B: They're ten euros ninety-nine.

2 A: _____ ?
   B: They're four euros ninety-nine.

3 A: _____ ?
   B: It's four euros fifty.

4 A: _____ ?
   B: They're fifteen euros ninety-nine.

5 A: _____ ?
   B: They're seventy-seven euros ninety-nine.

6 A: _____ ?
   B: They're twenty-two euros ninety-nine.

7 A: _____ ?
   B: They're eighteen euros fifty-nine.

8 A: _____ ?
   B: It's five euros ninety-nine.

Reading

7 Read the text and answer the questions. Use complete sentences.

My name is Ishan Kishore. I'm twenty-four and I'm from Mumbai in India. This is my market stall. It's also in Mumbai in Mangaldas Market. It's a clothes stall and it's open from Monday to Saturday. The clothes are for women: dresses, skirts and tops but no shoes or bags. Those red and pink dresses are very popular. They're 220 rupees – that's about €4. These skirts are very nice, too. They are yellow, blue or pink. They're 110 rupees – that's about €2.

1 What is Ishan's surname?
   His surname is Kishore .

2 How old is he?
   _____ .

3 Where is he from?
   _____ .

4 Where is his market stall?
   _____ .

5 What is on sale on his market stall?
   _____ .

6 When is his market stall open?
   _____ .

7 How much are the dresses?
   _____ .

8 What colour are the dresses?
   _____ .

9 How much are the skirts?
   _____ .

10 What colour are the skirts?
   _____ .

Vocabulary | irregular plurals

1 Write the plural for each word.

1 One child. Two _____ .
2 One woman. Two _____ .
3 One man. Two _____ .
4 One baby. Two _____ .
5 One person. Two _____ .
6 One wife. Two _____ .

Vocabulary | useful phrases

2 Complete the conversations with the words/phrases in the box.

> or   pay by credit card   Sign   That's
> Single or return?   PIN number   Can I

A: Can I help you?
B: Yes. Can I have a ticket to Manchester, please?
A: (1) _____
B: Return please.
A: That's £12.90, please.
B: Can I (2) _____ ?
A: Yes. (3) _____ here, please. Thank you.
B: Thank you.

C: Can I help you?
D: Yes. Can I have a packet of aspirin, please?
C: Twelve (4) _____ twenty-four?
D: Twelve please.
C: (5) _____ €1.09, please.
D: (6) _____ pay by credit card?
C: Certainly. Enter your (7) _____ , please. Thank you.
D: Thank you.

Grammar | possessive 's

3 Look at the table and write sentences.

	Sally	Julian	Petra	Mr Webber
House	modern	old	big	small
Children	7, 8 and 9 years old	12 and 14 years old	3 and 6 years old	2 and 3 years old
Car	red	blue	green	yellow
Parents	from Poland	from the UK	from Russia	from the US

1 (Julian/car) *Julian's car is blue*.
2 (Mr Webber/children) *Mr Webber's children are two and three years old*.
3 (Sally/house) _____ .
4 (Petra/parents) _____ .
5 (Mr Webber/house) _____ .
6 (Julian/children) _____ .
7 (Petra/car) _____ .
8 (Sally/parents) _____ .
9 (Julian/house) _____ .
10 (Petra/children) _____ .
11 (Sally/car) _____ .
12 (Julian/parents) _____ .

4 Look at the table in Ex. 3 again. Write questions using the words in **bold**.

1 *Is Sally's car blue*? **blue**
   No, it isn't. It's red.
2 _____ ? **2 and 3 years old**
   No, they aren't. They're three and six years old.
3 _____ ? **from the US**
   No, they aren't. They're from the UK.
4 _____ ? **big**
   No, it isn't. It's small.
5 _____ ? **from Russia**
   No, they aren't. They're from Poland.
6 _____ ? **blue**
   No, it isn't. It's green.
7 _____ ? **modern**
   No, it isn't. It's old.
8 _____ ? **12 and 14 years old**
   No, they aren't. They're two and three years old.

5 Answer the questions.

Dimitri	Katarina

Arabella	Armand

Giacomo	Larisa

1 Are they Dimitri's shoes?
No, they aren't. *They're Arabella's shoes*.

2 Is it Giacomo's coffee?
_____ . _____ .

3 Are they Katarina's children?
_____ . _____ .

4 Is it Larisa's hat?
_____ . _____ .

5 Are they Armand's books?
_____ . _____ .

6 Is it Arabella's orange juice?
_____ . _____ .

6 Read the sentences. What is the meaning of 's? Write P (possessive 's) or I (*is*).

1 Amado's my brother. [I]
2 Blanca's brother is Claudio.
3 Where is Keiko's bag?
4 Johann's not here today.
5 Who is Hilda's friend?
6 Jake's camera is great.
7 Karla's my friend.
8 Is Suzanne's surname Webber?

Listening

7 a `4.2` Cover the tapescript and listen. Match a conversation to a picture.

TAPESCRIPT

Conversation 1
A: Can I help you?
B: Yes. Can I have two tickets for the new Johnny Depp film, please?
A: *Red train*?
B: Yes, that's it.
A: Two adults?
B: No. One adult and one child, please.
A: OK, that's fifteen pounds fifty, please.
B: Can I pay by credit card?
A: Certainly.

Conversation 2
A: Good morning.
B: Good morning. Can I have a return to Birmingham, please?
A: Just one person?
B: Yes.
A: That's eighteen pounds ten, please.
B: Can I pay by credit card?
A: Of course.

Conversation ___

Ticket: to Brighton/to Birmingham
People: one person/two people
Price: £18.10/£80.10

Conversation ___

Film: Red Train/Red Ten
People: 1 adult and 1 child/2 adults
Tickets: £15.50/£16.50

b Listen again. Circle the correct words under each picture.

Grammar The verb *to be*

1 Complete the conversations with the correct form of the verb *to be*.

A: Good morning. Where (1) *are* you from?

B: (2) I_____ from Spain.

A: (3) _____ you from Madrid?

B: No, (4) I_____ . (5) I_____ from Jerez.

C: Hello. (6) _____ you Mr and Mrs Ferdinand?

D: No, we (7) _____ . (8) We_____ Mr and Mrs Mitchell.

C: Welcome to Hotel Franklin. Where (9) _____ your suitcases?

D: (10) They_____ in the taxi.

E: (11) _____ he your brother?

F: No, he (12) _____ . (13) He_____ my friend.

E: (14) _____ he from the US?

F: No, he (15) _____ . His mother and father (16) _____ from Ireland but he's from Scotland.

Possessive adjectives: *my, your, his, her, its, our, their*

2 Complete the sentences with the correct possessive adjective.

1 We are from Cornwall but *our* parents are from Liverpool.

2 _____ name is Steven Jones. He's an architect.

3 A: Hello. What's _____ name?

   B: I'm Tammy Smith.

4 I'm Olivia Emmerson and this is _____ husband, Greg.

5 Charles and Eva are our friends. _____ daughters are Debbie and Rachel.

6 It's a beautiful city and _____ tourist attractions are great.

7 Julia and _____ mother are on holiday in Australia.

8 They're in the Bergman Hotel. _____ room is number 458.

3 Write a negative sentence and a positive sentence from the prompts.

1 (we/teachers/students)
   We aren't teachers. We're students.

2 (it/ugly/beautiful)
   It's not ugly. It's beautiful.

3 (she/from Spain/from Italy)
   _____ .

4 (Paul and Tom/great singers/awful singers)
   _____ .

5 (I/Mrs Campbell/Miss Campbell)
   _____ .

6 (Joe/in the gallery/in the castle)
   _____ .

7 (You/23 years old/24 years old)
   _____ .

8 (You and I/good actors/great actors)
   _____ .

9 (He/from the UK/from Australia)
   _____ .

10 (It/my bag/your bag)
   _____ .

Verb *to be*: questions

4 Write questions and short answers with the prompts.

1 A: (they/engineers?) *Are they engineers*?

   B: (no) *No, they aren't* .

2 A: (she/your sister?) _____ ?

   B: (yes) _____ .

3 A: (I/in room 515?) _____ ?

   B: (no) _____ .

4 A: (it/your favourite restaurant?) _____ ?

   B: (yes) _____ .

5 A: (we/in your class?) _____ ?

   B: (no) _____ .

6 A: (he/from Spain?) _____ ?

   B: (yes) _____ .

7 A: (you/Pedro?) _____ ?

   B: (no) _____ .

8 A: (Ivan and Vlad/brothers?) _____ ?

   B: (yes) _____ .

Can I have ...?; How much ...?

5 Complete the conversations with questions.

A: (1) *How much are* the chicken sandwiches?

B: They're €3.59.

A: (2) _____ _____ _____ an orange juice?

B: It's €1.29.

A: (3) _____ _____ _____ _____ chicken sandwich and an orange juice, please?

B: Certainly. Anything else?

A: Yes. (4) _____ _____ _____ _____ black coffee, please?

C: (5) _____ _____ _____ the cheese salad sandwiches?

D: They're €3.29.

C: (6) _____ _____ _____ a piece of chocolate cake?

D: It's €1.89.

C: (7) _____ _____ _____ _____ piece of chocolate cake, please?

D: Certainly. Anything else?

C: No, thank you.

This, that, these, those

6 Circle the correct word.

1 *Those/This/These* is my brother.

2 Who are *that/this/those* people over there?

3 How much is *that/these/those* hat?

4 Is *this/those/these* your camera?

5 *That/These/This* are my favourite shops.

6 This blue skirt is €19.99 and *those/that/this* red skirts are €21.99.

7 Can I have *those/these/that* white bag, please?

8 Are *that/these/this* shoes from Italy?

possessive 's

7 Write questions with the prompts.

1 (What/Kieran/favourite film?)
   What is Kieran's favourite film?

2 (Who/Fiona/sister?)
   _____?

3 (Where/Miho/passport?)
   _____?

4 (they/Oliver/shoes?)
   _____?

5 (What/Jennifer/email address?)
   _____?

6 (Where/Lena/CD?)
   _____?

7 (Who/Harvey/manager?)
   _____?

8 (you/Leah/brother?)
   _____?

Vocabulary

8 Circle the odd one out.

1 orange   black   modern   blue

2 coat   skirt   Tuesday   T-shirt

3 ugly   old   children   good

4 Wednesday   Sunday   Friday   street

5 people   child   women   men

6 brother   book   camera   map

7 fourteen   thirty   film   twelve

8 green   dollar   white   brown

9 Complete the sentences with the circled words in Ex. 8.

1 Is it open on *Tuesday*?

2 It's one _____ ninety-nine.

3 What's your favourite _____ ?

4 My house is very _____ .

5 The café is on King _____ .

6 Are they your _____ ?

7 Is he your _____ ?

8 Who is that _____ ?

Vocabulary | city, countryside and coast

1 **a** Write *north*, *south*, *east*, *west* and *centre* in gaps 1–5 in the picture.

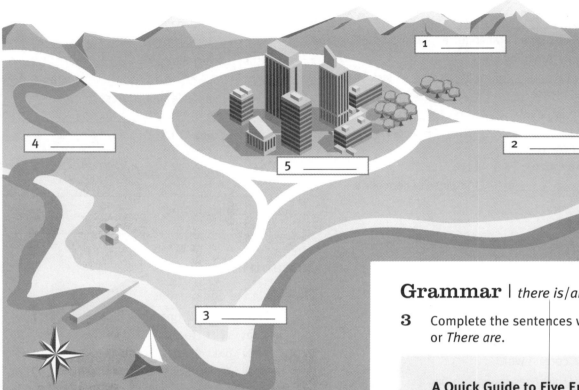

1 _____

2 _____

3 _____

4 _____

5 _____

b Look at the map in Ex. 1a again. Complete the sentences below with a word from the box.

> buildings   mountains   river   trees   beach

1 The _____ are in the centre of the city.
2 The _____ is in the south of the city.
3 The _____ is in the west of the city.
4 The _____ are in the north of the city.
5 The _____ are in the east of the city.

How to ... | give an opinion

2 Put the words in the correct order to make sentences.

1 is   think   this   beautiful.   I   beach
   I think this beach is beautiful .

2 city.   I   New York   great   think   a   is
   _____ .

3 think   those   I   ugly.   buildings   are
   _____ .

4 don't   manager.   a   Francis   is   think   good   I
   _____ .

5 beautiful   countryside   think   important   a
   good holiday.   I   for   is
   _____ .

Grammar | there is/are

3 Complete the sentences with *There's* or *There are*.

A Quick Guide to Five English Towns

Brighton
Brighton is only one hour from London.
(1) *There's* a beach near the centre of town and (2) _____ small shops and cafés in Brighton.

Canterbury
(3) _____ a famous cathedral in Canterbury and (4) _____ a beautiful river: the River Stour.

Nottingham
(5) _____ good shops and restaurants in Nottingham and (6) _____ a castle near the centre of town: Nottingham Castle.

York
York is very old and (7) _____ 600 year old streets in the town. (8) _____ also a famous Cathedral: York Minster.

Bristol
Bristol is in the west of England.
(9) _____ a beautiful bridge by Isambard Kingdom Brunel: the Clifton Suspension Bridge. (10) _____ also great museums and galleries.

4 Look at the website and write sentences with *There's* or *There are* + adjective.

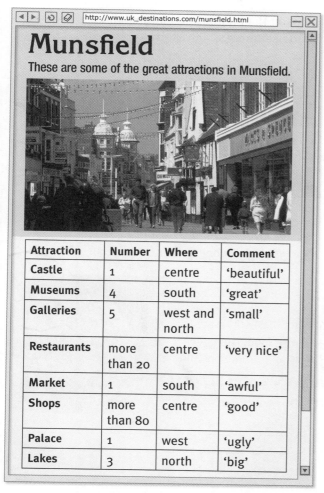

Munsfield

These are some of the great attractions in Munsfield.

Attraction	Number	Where	Comment
Castle	1	centre	'beautiful'
Museums	4	south	'great'
Galleries	5	west and north	'small'
Restaurants	more than 20	centre	'very nice'
Market	1	south	'awful'
Shops	more than 80	centre	'good'
Palace	1	west	'ugly'
Lakes	3	north	'big'

1 (galleries) *There are five small galleries in the west and north of Munsfield*.
2 (palace) _____ .
3 (museums) _____ .
4 (shops) _____ .
5 (market) _____ .
6 (restaurants) _____ .
7 (lakes) _____ .
8 (castle) _____ .

Vocabulary | *some, a lot of*

5 Rewrite the sentences in Ex. 4 with *a/an*, *some* or *a lot of*.

1 *There are some small galleries in the west and north of Munsfield*.
2 _____ .
3 _____ .
4 _____ .
5 _____ .
6 _____ .
7 _____ .
8 _____ .

Reading

6 Read about three language schools in the UK and complete the chart.

	Simon Says School of English	Partridge Tree English School	City Centre School of English
City	Cardiff		
Where		the east coast of England	
Classrooms			
Internet café			
Big tourist attractions			the city centre and the lochs

Language Schools

Name: Simon Says School of English

The Simon Says School of English is in Cardiff, the capital of Wales. There are fourteen classrooms and a canteen for students. There is an Internet café with ten computers. Cardiff is on the south coast of Wales. It's a great city and there are a lot of restaurants, shops and cafés. The big tourist attractions are Cardiff Castle, the Millennium Stadium in the city centre and the beautiful Welsh countryside.

Name: Partridge Tree English School

The Partridge Tree English School is near Norwich on the east coast of England. There are five classrooms and the classes are small – between seven and ten students. There is an Internet café next to the school and there is a cinema and a shopping centre near the school. The big tourist attractions are Norwich Cathedral and the Inspire Science Centre.

Name: City Centre School of English

The City Centre School of English is in Glasgow in Scotland. There are twenty-eight classrooms and forty teachers. There are two Internet cafés and a TV room for students. Glasgow is on the west coast of Scotland. The shops and galleries are great but the big tourist attractions are Glasgow city centre and the beautiful lakes (called 'Lochs'), for example Loch Lomond.

Vocabulary | prepositions of place

1 Find eight prepositions of place (one, two or three words) in the word grid.

i	a	g	b	u	r	f	s
n	e	x	t	t	o	d	u
f	x	u	n	l	o	o	n
r	c	o	n	z	a	h	d
o	p	p	o	s	i	t	e
n	m	p	j	s	n	y	r
t	q	n	e	a	r	u	h
o	a	l	k	d	g	m	b
f	d	b	e	h	i	n	d

2 Look at the picture. Complete the sentences below with a word/phrase from the box.

> behind ~~in~~ in front of opposite
> next to near under

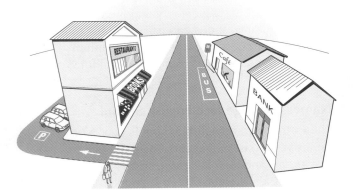

1 The man is *in* the café.
2 The café is _____ the bookshop.
3 The bus stop is _____ the café.
4 The car park is _____ the bookshop.
5 The bookshop is _____ the restaurant.
6 The bank is _____ the café.
7 The woman is _____ the bookshop.

Vocabulary | nationalities

3 Look at the photos and information. Write sentences.

Pierre: from France
Favourite food: from Italy
Car: from Japan

1 *Pierre's French.*
2 *His favourite food is Italian.*
3 *His car is Japanese.*

Yu Wan: from China
Favourite food: from India
Best friend: from Scotland

4 _____.
5 _____.
6 _____.

Angela: from Germany
Favourite food: from Russia
Husband: from Brazil

7 _____.
8 _____.
9 _____.

Telek: from Poland
Favourite food: from the US
Wife: from Australia

10 _____.
11 _____.
12 _____.

Grammar | *There isn't/aren't any; Is/Are there any ...*

4 Look at the shopping centre plan below. Complete the questions and answers.

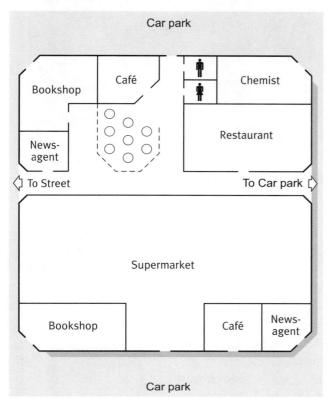

1 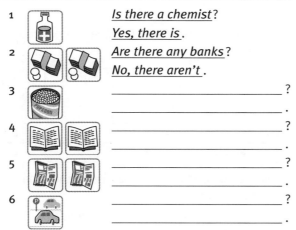 *Is there a chemist*?
   Yes, there is .

2 *Are there any banks* ?
   No, there aren't .

3 _____ ?
   _____ .

4 _____ ?
   _____ .

5 _____ ?
   _____ .

6 _____ ?
   _____ .

5 Write affirmative or negative sentences about the shopping centre in Ex. 4.

1 *There's a car park* . (car park)
2 *There aren't any galleries* . (galleries)
3 _____ . (restaurant)
4 _____ . (supermarket)
5 _____ . (department stores)
6 _____ . (train station)
7 _____ . (bookshops)
8 _____ . (museums)
9 _____ . (bank)
10 _____ . (cinemas)

Listening and reading

6 **5.1** Listen and write the questions below.

1 A: *Is there a hotel near here* ?
   B: Yes, there are two. There's a big hotel opposite the train station and there's a very nice hotel next to the cinema on Venice Road.
   A: Great, thanks.

2 A: Excuse me. _____ ?
   B: Err ... no, there aren't.
   A: Oh no!
   B: Sorry.
   A: Never mind.

3 A: Excuse me. _____ ?
   B: Yes, there is. There's one opposite the supermarket.
   A: Great. Thank you.
   B: You're welcome.

4 A: _____ . _____ ?
   B: Yes, there are. There's a café on Carnival Street, next to the supermarket and there's a restaurant opposite the cinema.
   A: Thank you!

7 Listen again and complete the map a–e below.

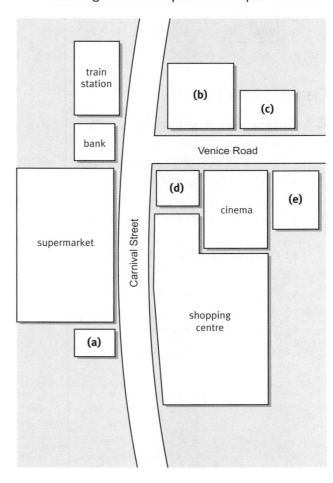

Vocabulary | abilities

1 Write a verb or phrase for each picture.

1. _dance_
2. _____
3. _____
4. _____
5. _____
6. _____
7. _____
8. _____

Grammar | can/can't

2 Write sentences with *can* and *can't*.

1. (I/sing ✓/play the piano ✗)
   I can sing but I can't play the piano.
2. (Jim and Jane/cook ✓/drive ✗)
   _____ .
3. (Loretta/swim ✗/use a computer ✓)
   _____ .
4. (You/play golf ✗/play the piano ✓)
   _____ .
5. (Sebastian/cook ✓/dance ✗)
   _____ .
6. (You and I/sing ✗/cook ✓)
   _____ .

3 Complete the conversation with the phrases in the box.

> They can   I can   Can he   can   Can you speak
> I can't   ~~can you~~   He can

A: So, Mrs Redwood, (1) _can you_ speak Italian?
B: (2) Yes, _____ . My mother and father are from Italy.
(3) _____ speak Italian, English, French and German.
A: Great. (4) _____ French and German?
B: I (5) _____ speak German but (6) _____ speak French.
A: That's OK. Mr Ploton is the manager. (7) _____ speak French.
B: (8) _____ speak English?
A: No, he can't.

4 Look at the table below. Complete the sentences, questions and answers.

	Jo	Simon	Leroy and Lena
speak Russian	✔	✗	✗
drive	✗	✔	✔
use a computer	✗	✔	✔

1. (Leroy and Lena/use a computer) Leroy and Lena
   can use a computer.
2. (Jo/use a computer) Jo _can't use a computer_ .
3. (Simon/drive?)
   A: _Can Simon drive_?
   B: _No, he can't_.
4. (Leroy and Lena/speak Russian) _____ .
5. (Jo/speak Russian?)
   A: _____ ?
   B: _____ .
6. (Simon/use a computer) _____ .
7. (Leroy and Lena/drive?)
   A: _____ ?
   B: _____ .
8. (Jo/drive) _____ .
9. (Simon/drive) _____ .

Listening

5 [5.2] Today is Linda's first day in her new job. Cover the tapescript below and listen. Complete the map of the office with the things in the box.

> Linda's desk   Edward's desk   Rachel's desk   Darren's desk

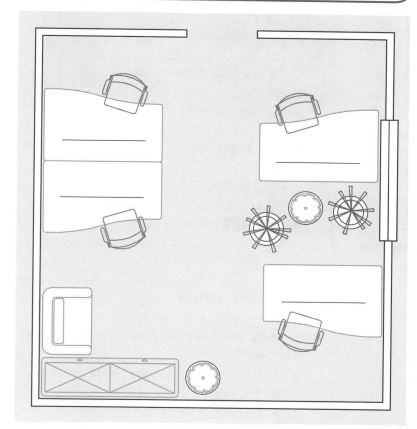

TAPESCRIPT

A: Welcome to North-South Travel.
B: Thank you.
A: I'm Edward Cole, your new manager.
B: Nice to meet you, Mr Cole.
A: Nice to meet you, too, Linda. What's your surname?
B: Brown.
A: OK. Well, please, call me Edward. So, it's your first day!
B: That's right.
A: Well, this is your desk. My desk is here, next to your desk. There's a computer and a telephone. Can you use a computer?
B: Yes, I can.
A: Great. Now, our main office is in Spain. Can you speak Spanish?
B: Yes, I can.
A: Good. And can you speak Italian? Some of our customers are from Italy.
B: No, I can't. But I can speak Russian.
A: Oh, that's great. I can speak Italian but I can't speak Russian.
That's Rachel's desk over there, next to the window and Darren's desk is over there, behind the plants.
B: Who's Darren?
A: Oh, he's our PA. He's great ...

6 Listen again. Make sentences about Edward and Linda using *can*.

1 Linda/use a computer
   She can use a computer.
2 Edward/speak Italian
   _____.
3 Linda/speak Spanish
   _____.
4 Linda/speak Russian
   _____.
5 Linda/speak Italian
   _____.
6 Edward/speak Russian
   _____.

Vocabulary | the time

7 Write the time next to each clock.

1  *ten o'clock*
2 **16:45** *quarter to five*
3 **06:30** _____
4 **21:50** _____
5 **11:20** _____
6 **01:00** _____
7 **20:30** _____
8 **06:15** _____
9 **17:35** _____
10 **05:05** _____

37

Vocabulary | adjectives to describe people

1 **a** Find five adjectives to describe people in the word square.

s	h	o	r	t
b	s	a	i	h
o	l	d	c	i
m	l	u	h	n
h	a	p	p	y

1 s _ _ _ _   3 o _ _   5 t _ _ _

2 r _ _ _   4 h _ _ _ _ _

b Match a word from Ex. 1a to the opposite below.

1 tall _____   4 poor _____

2 unhappy _____   5 young _____

3 fat _____

2 Label the picture below with the adjectives from Ex. 1a.

short   _____

_____   _____

_____   _____

_____   _____

Grammar 1 | Present Simple (1): *I like*

3 **a** Make sentences with *I like*/ *I don't like*.

1 (☺/cappuccino)

   I like cappuccino .

2 (☹/museums)

   I don't like museums .

3 (☺/rap music)

   _____ .

4 (☹/Arsenal Football Club)

   _____ .

5 (☺/computers)

   _____ .

6 (☹/Indian food)

   _____ .

7 (☹/espresso)

   _____ .

8 (☺/children)

   _____ .

9 (☺/James Bond films)

   _____ .

10 (☹/my manager)

   _____ .

b Write questions and answers for each word/ phrase in **bold**.

1 A: *Do you like black coffee*? **black coffee**

   B: Yes, *I do* .

2 A: *Do you like the countryside*? **the countryside**

   B: No, *I don't* .

3 A: _____ ? **Chinese food**

   B: Yes, _____ .

4 A: _____ ? **modern buildings**

   B: No, _____ .

5 A: _____ ? **salad**

   B: Yes, _____ .

6 A: _____ ? **supermarkets**

   B: No, _____ .

7 A: _____ ? **department stores**

   B: Yes, _____ .

8 A: _____ ? **American cars**

   B: No, _____ .

9 A: _____ ? **Harry Potter books**

   B: Yes, _____ .

10 A: _____ ? **The Beatles**

   B: No, _____ .

Grammar 2 | object pronouns

4 **a** Replace the <u>underlined</u> words with the correct object pronoun: *me, you, him, her, it, us* or *them*.

Now that I'm seventy …
by Harold Parks

Now that I'm 70, I am happy. A lot of people are my best friends. My children are my best friends. I like (1) <u>my children</u>. My sister is my best friend – I like (2) <u>my sister</u>. My brother is my best friend. I like (3) <u>my brother</u>. The television is my best friend. We are together every evening. I like (4) <u>the television</u>. And you are my best friend. I like (5) <u>you</u>. Do you like (6) <u>Harold Parks</u>?

b Replace the <u>underlined</u> words with the correct object pronoun or subject pronoun.

1 <u>You and</u> I are rich.   *We*
2 They like <u>you and I</u>.   _____
3 <u>Kevin and Callum</u> are engineers.   _____
4 Do you like <u>Kevin and Callum</u>?   _____
5 <u>Ella Fitzgerald</u> is my favourite singer. _____
6 I like <u>Ella Fitzgerald</u>.   _____
7 <u>Richard</u> is my best friend.   _____
8 I like <u>Richard</u>.   _____

Reading

5 Read the texts. Match a question from the box to each answer. Which question has two answers?

> Do you like big cities?
> Do you like holidays on the coast?
> Who are your favourite actors?
> What are your favourite things in life?
> Do you like British pop music?

_____ ?
Yes, I do – some of it. I like Keane and The Doves – they're great bands.

_____ ?
That's easy: Sean Penn, Halle Berry and Susan Sarandon. Sean Penn is great in *21 Grams*. It's a really good film.

Kimberley

_____ ?
Yes, I do. Paris, Buenos Aires and Rome are my favourites. Buenos Aires is fantastic.

_____ ?
I like French films, chocolate, coffee from Africa, the colour brown and Italian fashion, for example Versace.

Micaela

_____ ?
No, I don't, but I like holidays in the countryside. I think beach holidays are awful but holidays in, for example, the Cotswolds in the UK, now they're great.

_____ ?
That's a good question. I like Sunday mornings in bed, my friends and family and … a good book.

Peter

6.2

Vocabulary | jobs and activities

1 Write the job in each gap below.

1 *Designers* design things.

2 _____ cook food.

3 _____ build buildings.

4 _____ sell things.

5 _____ write articles.

6 _____ design buildings.

Grammar 1 | Present Simple (2): *we/they*

2 Look at the table and complete Grace's sentences.

	GRACE AND MARLON	STEVE AND SHENA
(1) like their job	YES	NO
(2) work in an office	YES	NO
(3) sell cars	NO	YES
(4) design cars	YES	NO

1 Grace: *We like our jobs.* *They don't like their jobs.*

2 Grace: _____ . _____ .

3 Grace: _____ . _____ .

4 Grace: _____ . _____ .

3 Complete the conversation with one word in each gap.

WEEKEND HOUSE SWAP
Two couples swap houses for a weekend and decorate!

Presenter: So, Sasha and Liam, what do you (1) *do*?
Sasha: (2) _____ designers. I'm a fashion designer and Liam is a car designer.
Presenter: And what about Colin and Nancy. What (3) _____ they do?
Liam: (4) _____ teachers. Colin is a primary school teacher and Nancy is a secondary school teacher.
Presenter: What do Colin and Nancy (5) _____ ?
Sasha: They like the coast and the countryside. (6) _____ like blues and greens in their house. They like boats and rivers but they (7) _____ like cities and they don't (8) _____ greys and blacks.
Presenter: (9) _____ do you like? Do (10) _____ like blues and greens in your house?
Liam: No, we (11) _____ . We like whites and greys. We like cities and towns. We (12) _____ the countryside and the coast, too, but just for a weekend.
Presenter: OK, thanks. Happy decorating!

Grammar 2 | *wh-* questions

4 **a** Add a word to complete each question.

1 What *do* you design?
2 _____ do you do?
3 Where _____ you live?
4 _____ do you work for?
5 _____ do you work?

b Complete the conversation with questions 1–5 from Ex. 4a.

Neil: Excuse me. Kate, this is Lance.

Kate: Hello Lance. Nice to meet you.

Lance: Nice to meet you, too.

Kate: (1) *What do you do*?

Lance: I'm a designer.

Kate: Oh really? (2) _____ ?

Lance: It's a company called Confident Designs.

Kate: (3) _____ ?

Lance: I design shoes and clothes.

Kate: Great! (4) _____ ?

Lance: In a small office in Manchester.

Kate: (5) _____ ?

Lance: In a house in a village near Manchester. What do you do?

Listening

5 **a** `6.1` Cover the tapescript below and listen. What job does each man do?

b Listen again. Complete the conversation.

TAPESCRIPT

Man 1:	Hi.
Man 2:	Hello.
F.A.:	Drink, sir?
Man 1:	Yes, (1) *can* I have an orange juice, please.
F.A.:	And for you, sir?
Man 2:	Can I (2) _____ a mineral water, please, sparkling. And an orange juice for my (3) _____ .
Man 1:	Thanks.
Man 2:	Thank you.
Man 1:	First time to New York?
Man 2:	(4) _____ ?
Man 1:	Is this your first time to New York?
Man 2:	Oh, no, it isn't. We (5) _____ to New York a lot for work. This is my wife, errr ... she's asleep.
Man 1:	No problem. (6) _____ do you do?
Man 2:	We (7) _____ coffee machines. We have a small company, it's (8) _____ company, and we sell coffee machines to restaurants, galleries, cafés, those kinds of places.
Man 1:	I see.
Man 2:	What do you (9) _____ ?
Man 1:	I'm an (10) _____ . I work for a big bank. Its offices are in the UK and the US – I travel a lot.
Man 2:	Yes, I see. Where do you live?
Man 1:	I live in New York with my family but a lot of the time I live in hotels ...

F.A. = Flight Attendant

6.3

Vocabulary | verbs of routine

1 a Match a verb 1–7 to a noun a–f.

1	watch	a)	to bed
2	start	b)	up
3	eat	c)	work
4	finish	d)	TV
5	go	e)	shower
6	get	f)	a sandwich
7	have a		

b Match a phrase in Ex. 1a to a picture below.

1 *get up*   5 _____
2 _____   6 _____
3 _____   7 _____
4 _____

Grammar | Present Simple (3): *he/she/it*

2 Look at the pictures in Ex. 1b. Write sentences.

1 *She gets up at 10.30*.
2 _____ .
3 _____ .
4 _____ .
5 _____ .
6 _____ .
7 _____ .

3 Make these sentences negative.

1 He eats chocolate. *He doesn't eat chocolate.*
2 She likes chicken.
3 William starts work early.
4 Teresa gets up at seven-thirty.
5 He goes to bed late.
6 She finishes work at five o'clock.
7 He watches TV every day.
8 Irene has a new job.

4 Read the text. Answer the questions.

1 Does Mrs Moody start work early? *Yes, she does*.
2 Does she have breakfast? _____ .
3 Does she drink coffee? _____ .
4 Does she go to the restaurant for lunch? _____ .
5 Does she finish work late? _____ .
6 Does she have any friends? _____ .

My manager is called Mrs Moody. She starts work at seven o'clock every morning. She doesn't have breakfast. She has a coffee at eleven o'clock. She has salad for lunch. She doesn't go to the restaurant – she eats her salad at her desk. She finishes work at about eight o'clock. She doesn't have any friends.

42

5 Write complete sentences.

1 (I/like/salad)
I like salad .

2 (Cheryl/finish/her English class/half past ten)
Cheryl finishes her English class at half past
ten .

3 (They/work/in a restaurant)
_____ .

4 (Hilary and Ben/not/eat fast food)
_____ .

5 (Connor/not/eat salad)
_____ .

6 (you/go to bed early?)
_____ ?

7 (Uma/like/me?)
_____ ?

8 (What/she/do?)
_____ ?

Listening

6 `6.2` Cover the text and listen. Complete the
table. ✓ = like/love; ✗ = don't/doesn't like.

	me	Billy	Bianca	Larry and Mel
me		✓		
Billy				
Bianca				
Larry and Mel				

So ... my family is a bit strange.
There's my husband, Billy, my
best friend, Bianca, and my
parents, Larry and Mel. Now I
love Billy, of course, and Billy
loves me. But Billy doesn't like
Bianca. I don't know why but
he doesn't. And Bianca doesn't
like him. She likes my parents,
and they like her, but they don't
like Billy. And, you know what,
Billy doesn't like them. Now,
of course, I like Bianca and my
parents and they all like me.
But Billy isn't popular.

Writing

7 Complete the letter to a friend with the phrases
in the box.

How are you?
and my team like me.
~~89 Gilhurst Road,~~
Dear Stephen,
Please write and tell me your news.
Best wishes,
2nd December

Flat 15
(1) *89 Gilhurst Road*
Plymouth

(2) _____

(3) _____

(4) _____ I hope you're well.

I have a new job: I'm still with Copy
Fast but I'm a manager now. I get up
early and I work late but I like my job
(5) _____

David, the old manager, is a sales rep
now. He works for a small company. He
doesn't like his new job. He starts
work early and he drives all over the
country.

(6) _____
(7) _____
Gareth

there is/are; there isn't/aren't; Is/ Are there ...?

1 Complete the conversation with *there's, there is, there isn't, there are, there aren't, Is there* or *Are there*.

A: Good morning. (1) *Is there* a bank near here?

B: Yes, (2) _____ . It's on Parliament Street.

A: And (3) _____ any museums near here?

B: Yes, (4) _____ . (5) _____ a small museum on Baker Street and (6) _____ a big museum opposite the train station.

C: Hello. (7)_____ any good restaurants in town?

D: Yes, (8) _____ . (9) _____ a good Japanese restaurant on Gatson Street and (10) _____ two good Indian restaurants on Mile Road.

C: Great. And (11) _____ a cashpoint in this hotel?

D: No, (12) _____ .

E: Good afternoon. (13) _____ any supermarkets near here?

F: No, (14) _____ .

E: (15) _____ a newsagent near here?

F: Yes, (16) _____ . It's next to the cinema.

can/can't

2 Rearrange the words to make sentences and questions.

1 daughter Can drive. your
   Can your daughter drive?

2 can't Steven piano. the play
   _____ .

3 Spanish. speak They can
   _____ .

4 you a use Can computer?
   _____ ?

5 dance. can sing and Michelle
   _____ .

6 cook. husband My can't
   _____ .

Present Simple

3 Complete the sentence with the verb in brackets in the Present Simple.

1 Gary is a chef. He *cooks* (cook) Italian food in a restaurant.

2 My parents *don't get up* (not get up) late.

3 I _____ (like) British pop music.

4 We're designers. We _____ (design) magazines.

5 Sophie _____ (not eat) meat.

6 Sebastian _____ (eat) a lot of salad.

7 Alex _____ (not like) football.

8 You _____ (finish) work late.

9 We are writers. We _____ (write) newspaper articles.

10 Brian and Tara _____ (watch) TV in the evening.

11 Harry's sister _____ (love) your house.

12 Graham _____ (start) work at 10 o'clock.

4 Write questions and answers from the prompts.

1 (you/play tennis) (yes)
   A: *Do you play tennis*? **B:** *Yes, I do*.

2 (your sisters/like your wife) (no)
   A: _____ ? **B:** _____ .

3 (Davina/eat a lot) (yes)
   A: _____ ? **B:** _____ .

4 (they/sell houses) (yes)
   A: _____ ? **B:** _____ .

5 (Felix/love her) (no)
   A: _____ ? **B:** _____ .

6 (your friends/live in Barcelona) (yes)
   A: _____ ? **B:** _____ .

7 (Craig/eat fast food) (no)
   A: _____ ? **B:** _____ .

8 (we/have any food in the house) (no)
   A: _____ ? **B:** _____ .

9 (you/design clothes) (yes)
   A: _____ ? **B:** _____ .

10 (Virginia/have a brother) (yes)
   A: _____ ? **B:** _____ .

Object pronouns: *me, you, him, her, it, us, them*

5 Complete the gaps with *me, you, him, her, it, us, them*.

1 He's my best friend. I really like *him* .
2 You're my brother but I don't like _____ .
3 They're great. We like _____ .
4 It's an ugly city. I don't like _____ .
5 I'm very happy. She loves _____ .
6 She's my manager. I don't like _____ .
7 We like them and they like _____ .

Telling the time

6 Write the times in full.

1 *quarter to four*

2 _____

3 _____

4 _____

5 _____

6 _____

7 _____

8 _____

9 _____

10 _____

Vocabulary

7 Complete the gaps with the nationalities of the countries in brackets.

1 In Brazil people speak *Portuguese*. (Portugal)
2 Do you like _____ food? (China)
3 BMW is a _____ car company. (Germany)
4 Giorgio Armani is an _____ fashion designer. (Italy)
5 There are a lot of _____ restaurants in the UK. (India)
6 Can you speak _____ ? (Poland)
7 Ibiza is a beautiful _____ island. (Spain)
8 Mercedes Sosa is a famous _____ singer. (Argentina)

8 Complete the sentences with the opposite of the adjective in **bold**.

1 He's not **rich**, he's *poor*.
2 She's not **old**, she's _____ .
3 They're not **fat**, they're _____ .
4 I'm not **tall**, I'm _____ .
5 We're not **sad**, we're _____ .

9 Match a verb 1–8 to a word or phrase a–h.

1 use   a) an article
2 write   b) to bed
3 play   c) TV
4 design   d) dinner
5 finish   e) the piano
6 cook   f) a computer
7 go   g) work
8 watch   h) a building

Vocabulary | people and places

1 Complete the crossword with the names of the places 1–8.

```
              1
              C
        2     A
   3          L
      4       L
              [ ]
5             C
              E
   6          N
              T
7             R
              E
8
```

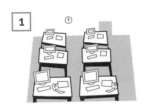

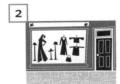

2 Write one job for each place in Ex. 1.

1 _call centre_ = _call centre worker_
2 _____ = _____
3 _____ = _____
4 _____ = _____
5 _____ = _____
6 _____ = _____
7 _____ = _____
8 _____ = _____

Grammar | imperatives

3 a Write an imperative next to each picture. Use the word in brackets.

1 (quiet) _____

2 (down) _____

3 (watch) _____

4 (line) _____

5 (look) _____

6 (in) _____

b Write the opposite of each imperative in Ex. 3a. Use _Please_.

1 _Please don't be quiet_.
2 _____ .
3 _____ .
4 _____ .
5 _____ .
6 _____ .

How to ... | make a business phone call

4 7.1 Listen to these business phone calls. Write in the missing phrases.

1

PA: Good morning. WP Graphics.

Woman: Good morning. (1) *Can I speak to* Andrew Holden, please?

PA: Certainly. (2) _____ . ...

PA: Hello.

Woman: Hello.

PA: I'm sorry but Mr Holden (3) _____ at the moment. Can I take a message?

Woman: No, thank you. I can call back later.

PA: OK. Thank you. Bye.

Woman: Bye.

2

PA: Hello. Marshall and Smith Accountants.

Mr Eames: Hello. Can I speak to Mrs Marshall, please?

PA: (4) _____ .

Mrs Marshall: Hello. Sarah Marshall.

Mr Eames: Hello, Mrs Marshall. It's Anthony Eames.

Mrs Marshall: Hello, Mr Eames. (5) _____ ?

Mr Eames: Well ...

3

PA: Good afternoon. North Stone University.

Ted: Hello. (6) _____ , please.

PA: Certainly. Hold the line, please.

Karen: Hello.

Ted: Hello, Karen. (7) _____ .

Karen: Hello, Ted. How are you?

Ted: Fine, thanks. And you?

Karen: Not bad. Busy as always. (8) _____ ?

Ted: Well, I have a small problem and ...

Vocabulary | months

5 **a** Complete the months below. Put them in the correct order.

J _ l y   [   ]
_ c t _ b _ r   [   ]
J _ n _ _ r y   [1]
D _ c _ m b _ r   [   ]
_ _ g _ s t   [   ]
M _ y   [   ]
_ p r _ l   [   ]
F _ b r _ _ r _   [   ]
N _ v _ m b _ r   [   ]
J _ n _   [   ]
S _ p t _ m b _ r [   ]
M _ r c h   [   ]

b Cover the months above. What month is the birthday of each celebrity below?

1 Maria Sharapova (19/04/1987) *April*
2 Giorgio Armani (11/07/1934) _____
3 Stephen Hawking (08/01/1942) _____
4 Roger Federer (08/08/1981) _____
5 John Travolta (18/02/1954) _____
6 Bruce Springsteen (23/09/1949) _____
7 Woody Allen (1/12/1935) _____
8 Bono (10/05/1960) _____
9 Angelina Jolie (04/06/1975) _____
10 Sting (02/10/1951) _____
11 Brooklyn Beckham (04/03/1999) _____
12 Condoleezza Rice (14/11/1954) _____

Vocabulary | work phrases

1 **a** Circle the correct verb.

1 *work* / *call* / *write* customers
2 *answer* / *have* / *write* the phone
3 *work* / *travel* / *write* reports
4 *call* / *work* / *take* work home
5 *give* / *work* / *travel* from home
6 *work* / *give* / *have* outdoors
7 *call* / *give* / *answer* presentations
8 *answer* / *travel* / *have* abroad
9 *have* / *write* / *work* meetings

b Match the verb phrases above to the pictures below.

Grammar | adverbs of frequency

2 **a** Put the words in the box in the correct place.

~~often~~ never sometimes usually
not often/not usually always

100% a _____
         b _____
         c *often*
         d _____
         e _____
0%   f _____

b Put the words in the correct order to make sentences.

1 afternoon. watch TV never I in the

_____ .

2 work Maggie usually home. doesn't take

_____ .

3 We outdoors. work sometimes

_____ .

4 to always go Do bed you at 11 o'clock?

_____ .

5 golf He Sundays. often plays on

_____ .

6 abroad. They travel don't often

_____ .

3 Write the adverb of frequency in the correct place.

1 I swim in the sea. (not often)
   I don't often swim in the sea.

2 I'm late for work. (sometimes)

_____ .

3 I drive. (never)

_____ .

4 I sing and play the piano at family parties. (usually)

_____ .

5 My manager answers the phone at work. (not usually)

_____ .

6 He is happy on Friday afternoons. (always)

_____ .

Reading

4 a Read the three texts. Match a text to a person.

1 Regina doesn't work in an office. She talks to customers a lot but she doesn't usually call them. She never works from home and she doesn't take work home. She always works on Saturdays. She doesn't give presentations or write reports and she doesn't use a computer.

Regina: 'I like my job. I always start work at nine and finish at five. I don't think about my job after 5 o'clock.'

2 Darcy doesn't work in an office and she doesn't work in a school. She sometimes starts work in the morning, sometimes in the afternoon and sometimes at night. She often works at weekends. In Darcy's job there aren't any customers but she talks to people every day.

Darcy: 'I love my job. I don't take work home. I like the doctors but I don't like the nights.'

3 Olivia doesn't work in a factory or a call centre. She starts work at nine and finishes at five every day. She never works on weekends. She doesn't call customers but she often has meetings with her manager and sends a lot of emails. She sometimes takes work home in the evenings.

Olivia: 'My job is OK. I don't love it and I don't hate it. My manager is quite nice.'

b Read the texts again. Complete the gaps with the name of a person in the photos.

1 _____ never works on Saturday.
2 _____ works in an office.
3 _____ doesn't start work at 9 o'clock every day.
4 _____ and _____ never call customers.
5 _____ works in a shop.
6 _____ and _____ never take work home.
7 _____ works in a hospital.
8 _____ uses a computer at work.

Writing

5 Put the phrases in the box in the correct order to make a note.

> call me at home   My phone number
> Can you   Thanks,   ~~Hi Jared~~
> Dilara   this afternoon?   is 04931 829319.

Hi Jared

Vocabulary | ordinal numbers and dates

1   **a** Complete the crossword with the clues below.

Across	Down
2) 4th	1) 5th
5) 30th	3) 12th
7) 11th	4) 15th
10) 19th	6) 20th
11) 8th	8) 1st
12) 3rd	9) 2nd

b Put the dates in written form.

1   the twenty-first of January   *21st January*
2   the eleventh of March   _____
3   the first of May   _____
4   the twelfth of December   _____
5   the twentieth of June   _____
6   the sixteenth of November   _____
7   the second of September   _____
8   the third of February   _____

Grammar | *would like*

2   **a** Complete the conversation with phrases from the box.

> What would you like   I'd like a
> thank you   ~~What would you like to~~
> Would you like   I'd like

A: Hello, Mr Wallace. My name's Orla Birch.
B: Hello, Ms. Birch. This is Mrs Trenter.
A: Nice to meet you, Mrs Trenter.
C: Nice to meet you, too.
A: Please, come into my office. (1) *What would you like to* drink?
B: (2) _____ coffee, please.
C: And I'd like a cup of tea, please.
A: (3) _____ milk and sugar?
B: No, (4) _____ . Just black.
C: Yes, please.
A: (5) _____ to eat? A piece of cake?
B: I'd like some fruit, please.
C: (6) _____ a piece of cake. Thank you.

b Write questions and answers with the words in **bold**.

1   **A:** *Would you like a black coffee*? **black coffee**
    B: *No, thank you*. **No**
2   **A:** *What would you like to eat*? **to eat**
    B: *I'd like a sandwich, please*. **sandwich**
3   **A:** _____ ? **mineral water**
    B: _____ . **No**
4   **A:** _____ ? **orange juice**
    B: _____ . **Yes**
5   **A:** _____ ? **to drink**
    B: _____ . **espresso**
6   **A:** _____ ? **piece of cake**
    B: _____ . **Yes**
7   **A:** _____ ? **to eat**
    B: _____ . **a salad**
8   **A:** _____ ? **instant coffee**
    B: _____ . **No**

Vocabulary | food

3 **a** Rearrange the letters to make a kind of food.

1   s g e e t l v a b e   _vegetables_

2   o p s u   s_____

3   d l a a s   s_____

4   k i n d r s   d_____

5   t r u i f   f_____

6   s s e e r t s d   d_____

7   s s k c n a   s_____

8   r s t t r a e   s_____

9   a c m i s u r o n e   m_____   c_____

b Complete the text below with a word from Ex. 3a.

When I go to a restaurant, I always have a

 _____ , for example chicken

 _____ and I never have any

 _____ before the meal.

For a  _____ I usually order an

Italian dish, for example spaghetti bolognese with a

 _____ or some fresh

_____ .

I never have any _____ but sometimes I

order a plate of fresh _____ . I don't

have soft _____ – just a mineral water.

Listening

4 **7.2** Cover the tapescript below and listen. Choose the correct picture for each conversation.

TAPESCRIPT

1

A: What would you like?

B: Err ... I'd like vegetable soup and ... a chicken salad, please.

A: Here you are.

B: Thanks.

2

A: Hello Mr Adams. Welcome to our factory.

B: Thank you.

A: Would you like a coffee?

B: Yes, please. White, two sugars, please.

A: Is instant coffee OK?

B: Yes, that's fine.

3

A: OK, before the meeting, what would you like to drink?

B: Can I have a cup of tea, please?

A: Sure. Would you like a piece of cake? A biscuit?

B: A piece of cake, please.

A: Chocolate cake?

B: Great.

Conversation 1

A   B

Conversation 2

C   D

Conversation 3

E   F

8.1 Leisure

Vocabulary | leisure activities

1 a Match a word in the box to a picture.

> tennis swimming reading eat
> television cycling football ~~chess~~
> theatre walking sightseeing exercise

1 *chess* 7 _____

2 _____ 8 _____

3 _____ 9 _____

4 _____ 10 _____

5 _____ 11 _____

6 _____ 12 _____

b Write the phrase for each leisure activity in the pictures above.

1 *play chess*
2 *watch television*
3 *do exercise*
4 _____
5 _____
6 _____
7 _____
8 _____
9 _____
10 _____
11 _____
12 _____

How to ... | talk about things to do

2 Look at the table and complete the conversation.

	Jeff's house	Adelina's house	Pia's house
television	✓	✓	✓
chess	✓	✗	✓
tennis	✗	✓	✗
swimming	✗	✗	✓
exercise	✗	✓	✗

A: Where do you want to go this weekend?

B: How about Jeff's house. (1) *You can watch* TV and (2) _____ _____ _____ chess at his house.

A: Yeah, but I want to do some exercise. What about Adelina's house? (3) _____ _____ _____ tennis and (4) _____ _____ _____ exercise.

B: But I want to swim. How about Pia's house. (5) _____ _____ _____ swimming at her house. She's got a swimming pool.

A: Good idea.

Grammar | like + -ing; want + infinitive

3 Complete the sentences with *want* or *like*.

1 Marcus and Pete *want* to play football.
2 Do you _____ eating out?
3 Which restaurant do you _____ to go to?
4 They don't _____ watching TV.
5 Does she _____ playing tennis?
6 Do you _____ to go for a walk?
7 I don't _____ playing chess.
8 We _____ to go to the theatre.

4 Complete the texts with the verbs in brackets.

My name is Kate Watson. I'm a chef. I work for a small restaurant called *The Happy Chicken*. I like (1) *being* (be) a chef and I like (2) _____ (work) with food but I don't like (3) _____ (finish) work at one o'clock in the morning. I want (4) _____ (work) from nine to five and I want (5) _____ (go) out with my friends in the evening. I never see my friends – I'm always at work!

My name is Johan Holland. I'm a call centre worker. I like (6) _____ (work) with lots of people but I don't like my job. It's not exciting. I want (7) _____ (be) a sales rep. I like (8) _____ (travel) abroad and I like (9) _____ (sell) things. I don't want (10) _____ (call) customers for eight hours a day.

Vocabulary | adjectives

5 a Rearrange the letters to make six adjectives.

1 iiucfdftl = d_____   4 nuf = f_____
2 yase = e_____   5 netgixic = e_____
3 igrobn = b_____   6 sirtintegne = i_____

b Complete the sentences with adjectives 1–6 above.

1 I don't like having meetings at work. I want to sleep in meetings. They're _____ .
Uri Anderson, 42, Sales Manager

2 I can speak Russian, English and Spanish. Languages are very _____ for me.
Asenka Chazov, 14, Student

3 I read two or three books every week. Books are very _____ .
Armina Lang, 49, Lecturer

4 I got 3 out of 20 in my maths test. Maths is very _____ for me.
Edel Möller, 16, Student

5 I like travelling abroad and meeting new people. It's _____ .
Vashti Adamski, 26, Reporter

6 I go out with friends from work every Friday evening. It's _____ .
Josie West, Designer

Writing

6 Look at the advert below. Complete the email to the hotel.

Manor Bridge Hotel
A beautiful hotel in the heart of the English countryside.

- 6 double rooms
- 2 single rooms
- swimming pool
- much more!

Come to Manor Bridge Hotel for a weekend away or a holiday!

manorhotel@burbank.net

tennis court too???

breakfast included???

From: percycotton@worldwidemail.com
To: (1) _____
Subject: room for December 18th/19th

Dear (2) _____
I (3) _____ some more information about your hotel.

- Do you have a (4) _____ room available for my wife and I on (5) _____ ?
- (6) _____ is it for two nights?
- Is breakfast (7) _____ ?
- Has the hotel got (8) _____

I (9) _____ to your reply.
Yours (10) _____ ,
Percy Cotton

Vocabulary | rooms and furniture

1 a Match a piece of furniture in the box to a picture.

> washing machine ~~sofa~~ fridge
> coffee table car wardrobe bed
> mirror basin bath armchair cooker
> toilet sink

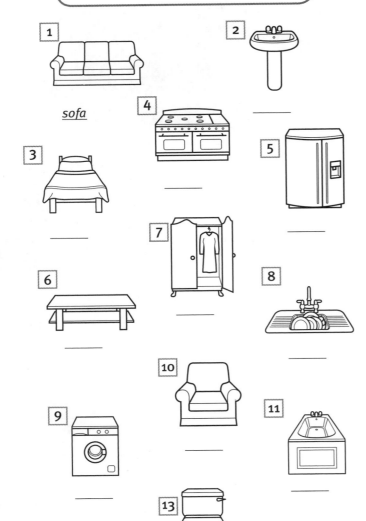

sofa

b Match the furniture in Ex. 1a to a room below.

Bathroom: _____ _____ _____
Bedroom: _____ _____ _____
Kitchen: _washing machine_ _____ _____
  _____
Living room: _____ _____ _____
Garage: _____

Grammar | have got/has got

2 a Look at the chart. Complete the text below for Jamie.

	Jamie	Patricia
bedrooms	1	2
garage	✗	✓
garden	✗	✗
washing machine	✓	✗
bath	✗	✓
sofa	✓	✓
car	✓	✗

(1) '_I've got_ a small flat in Notting Hill in the UK. (2) It _____ one bedroom and a living room. It (3) _____ a garage or a garden. I (4) _____ a washing machine in the kitchen and a sofa in the living room. I (5) _____ a bath – just a shower. I (6) _____ a car – it's a small, red sports car.'

b Look at the chart. Complete the text below about Patricia.

(1) _She's got_ a house in Auckland in New Zealand. It (2) _____ two bedrooms and a garage but it (3) _____ a garden. She (4) _____ a bath in the bathroom and a sofa in the living room. She (5) _____ a washing machine and she (6) _____ a car.

3 Complete the conversation.

A: Hello. Can I help you?

C: No, thank you. I'm just looking.

A: Our televisions are on special offer today. (1) _____ you _____ a television?

C: Yes, I (2) _____ .

A: (3) _____ you _____ a television in your bedroom?

C: No, I (4) _____ . But I don't want a television. I want a washing machine for my mother.

A: (5) _____ your mother _____ a television in her bedroom?

C: Yes, she (6) _____ . Now, how much is this washing machine.

A: It's £399. The television is only £299 ...

4 Write complete sentences with *have got*.

1 (you/a car?) (Yes)
A: *Have you got a car?*
B: *Yes, I have*.

2 (Ravi/✓/a new house)
Ravi's got a new house.

3 (My parents/✗/a washing machine)

_____ .

4 (your house/a garage?) (No)
A: _____ ?
B: _____ .

5 (that hotel/a swimming pool?) (Yes)
A: _____ ?
B: _____ .

6 (my hotel room/✗/bath)

_____ .

7 (we/✓/a new baby)

_____ .

8 (you/✓/a beautiful flat)

_____ .

9 (my sisters/✗/any children)

_____ .

10 (we/any milk in the fridge?) (Yes)
A: _____ ?
B: _____ .

Listening

5 **a** `8.1` Listen and mark the stress.

1 I've <u>got</u> a <u>new</u> <u>bi</u>cycle.
2 Have you got a big fridge?
3 Mark hasn't got my email address.
4 Have your friends got televisions in their bedrooms?
5 They haven't got a coffee table.
6 She's got a nice sofa.

b Listen again and repeat.

Reading

6 Read the texts and answer the questions.

I want to live in ...

This week we talk to Oscar O'Connor, actor, singer and writer.

I want to live in St Petersburg in Russia. It's not the capital of Russia but it's Russia's cultural capital. It's interesting and exciting ... I love it.

St Petersburg is in the west of Russia. It's only 300 years old but it has got a lot of beautiful buildings, for example The Hermitage and The Summer Palace. Nevsky Prospect is the main street in St Petersburg. It's got a lot of shops and restaurants.

My favourite place is St Issak Cathedral. It's got amazing views of the city from the top and inside it's got beautiful paintings. It's also got a cashpoint!

My friends live in St Petersburg and they've got a nice flat near the centre of the city. They haven't got a garden but they've got a dacha! It's a small house in the countryside for holidays or the weekend.

1 Is St Petersburg the capital of Russia?
No, it isn't.

2 How old is it?

_____ .

3 What is the main street?

_____ .

4 What is Oscar's favourite place?

_____ .

5 What is in St Isaak Cathedral?

_____ .

6 Where do Oscar's friends go for weekends and holidays?

_____ .

How to ... | make suggestions

1 Complete the conversation with *What about ...?* or *How about ...?* and a phrase from the box.

> a swim in the lake
> a game of chess
> that new café on Cathedral Street
> a film at the cinema
> ~~a game of tennis~~

A: What do you want to do this afternoon?

B: *How about a game of tennis*?

A: No. I don't like playing tennis.

B: _____
_____ ?

A: No. I don't like swimming.

B: _____
_____ ?

A: No. I don't want to go to a café.

B: _____
_____ ?

A: No. I can't play chess.

B: _____
_____ ?

A: Good idea. Which film?

Grammar | question words

2 Complete each question with the correct question word.

1 **A:** *What* do you teach?
  B: I teach English.

2 **A:** _____ is your favourite actor?
  B: Jean Claude Van Damme.

3 **A:** _____ far is your school?
  B: It's about 2km from here.

4 **A:** _____ is Jackie?
  B: She's in the bathroom.

5 **A:** _____ Elvis song is this?
  B: It's *You Are Always on my Mind*.

6 **A:** _____ old is she?
  B: She's eighty-two.

7 **A:** _____ is your teacher?
  B: Mrs Malkmus.

8 **A:** _____ coffee table do you like?
  B: I like this coffee table. It's nice.

3 Read the texts then write a question for each answer.

Kathleen Stock is a university lecturer from Cork in Ireland. She's 42 years old and she works for Dublin City University. Her husband is Tom Stock.

1 *What is her surname*?
  Stock.

2 _____ ?
  She's a university lecturer.

3 _____ ?
  Cork in Ireland.

4 _____ ?
  42.

5 _____ ?
  Dublin City University.

6 _____ ?
  He's her husband.

Iznik is a small restaurant in Bristol. It serves excellent Turkish food. A typical meal costs £15. The owner is a woman called Ceylan Yildirim. She's from Bodrum in Turkey.

7 _____ ?
  Iznik.

8 _____ ?
  Turkish food.

9 _____ ?
  Bristol.

10 _____ ?
   £15

11 _____ ?
   Ceylan Yildirim

12 _____ ?
   Bodrum in Turkey.

Vocabulary | food

4 Complete the puzzle with kinds of food. Find the hidden phrase.

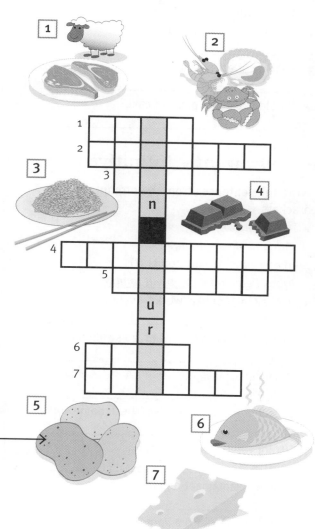

Listening

5 **a** Complete the conversation with a word in each gap.

Waiter: Hello. *Gino's* restaurant.
Sam: Hello. I'd (1) _____ to book a table for Saturday evening.
Waiter: Certainly, madam. (2) _____ many people?
Sam: Two.
Waiter: What (3) _____ ?
Sam: Nine o'clock, please.
Waiter: And what's the name, please?
Sam: Sam Allman.
Waiter: OK, that's fine, Ms Allman. (4) _____ you on Saturday.
Sam: Thank you. Goodbye.

b **8.2** Listen and check your answers.

6 Complete the conversation with a word in each gap.

Waiter: Hello, madam. Do you have a (1) _____ ?
Sam: Yes, I do. My name's Sam Allman.
Waiter: Ms Allman. A (2) _____ for two?
Sam: Yes, that's right.
Waiter: (3) _____ with me, please.

Waiter: Are you (4) _____ to order?
Sam: Yes. I'd (5) _____ chicken soup, please, and fish curry.
Waiter: Certainly, madam. And for you, sir?
Tony: Can I (6) _____ seafood pasta, please? No starter, thank you.
Waiter: Certainly. What would you like to (7) _____ ?
Sam: Can I have an orange juice, please?
Tony: And I'd like a mineral water, please.
Waiter: (8) _____ or sparkling?
Tony: Sparkling, please.

Sam: Excuse me. Can I have the (9) _____ , please?
Waiter: Of course.

b **8.3** Listen and check your answers.

Imperatives

1 Match a word or phrase 1–8 to a word or phrase a–h to make an imperative.

1 Sit
2 Turn
3 Listen
4 Be
5 Hold
6 Don't come
7 Don't look
8 Don't eat

a) the line, please.
b) off your mobile phone.
c) down, please.
d) chocolate for lunch.
e) at my emails.
f) quiet, please.
g) in.
h) to me, please.

Adverbs of frequency

2 Put the adverb of frequency in brackets into the correct place in the sentence.

1 I turn off my mobile phone. (never)
I never turn off my mobile phone.

2 I'm late. (sometimes)
_____.

3 Do you work from home? (often)
_____?

4 Are they happy? (always)
_____?

5 I have a coffee in the morning. (usually)
_____.

6 Do you play chess? (sometimes)
_____?

7 She is early. (not usually)
_____.

8 They listen to me. (never)
_____.

would like

3 Correct the mistake in each sentence.

1 What would you like eat?   *to*
What would you like to eat?

2 Would like a cup of tea?
_____.

3 I like a coffee, please.
_____.

4 Would like you a piece of cake?
_____.

like + ing; want + infinitive

4 Write full sentences from the prompts in brackets.

1 (Adriana/like/sing)
Adriana likes singing.

2 (Peter/want/go out tonight?)
Does Peter want to go out tonight?

3 (My sister/not like/work from home)
_____.

4 (Jerome and Kay/not want/go swimming)
_____.

5 (Alan/like/play golf)
_____.

6 (teachers/not usually like/check homework)
_____.

7 (I/not want/cook tonight)
_____.

8 (Kiefer/want/meet Julia)
_____.

9 (you/like/work from home?)
_____?

10 (Sheila and Jeff/like/watch TV?)
_____?

have got/has got

5 Complete the conversation with the correct form of have got.

Petra: (1) *Have* you *got* a house or a flat?
Julia: I (2) _____ _____ a house.
Petra: (3) _____ it _____ a garage?
Julia: No, it (4) _____ . I (5) _____ _____ a new car but I (6) _____ _____ a garage.
Petra: (7) _____ you _____ a garden?
Julia: No, I (8) _____ . But my friends (9) _____ _____ a garden and I sometimes go there. They (10) _____ _____ a swimming pool in their garden.
Petra: (11) _____ they _____ a tennis court?
Julia: Yes, they (12) _____ .

Question words

6 Circle the correct question word.
1 *What / Where / Who* do you work?
2 *What / Where / Who* do you work for?
3 *What / Where / Who* music do you like?
4 *How / Which / Who* near is it?
5 *How / Which / Where* restaurant do you want to go to?
6 *What / Which / Where* do you do?

Dates

7 How do we say and write dates? Complete the gaps below.

1 **Say:** the fourteenth of August
  Write: *14th August*
2 **Say:** _____
  Write: 1st September
3 **Say:** the twenty-third of November
  Write: _____
4 **Say:** _____
  Write: 22nd January
5 **Say:** the eleventh of March
  Write: _____
6 **Say:** _____
  Write: 31st June
7 **Say:** the eighth of February
  Write: _____
8 **Say:** _____
  Write: 12th April

Making suggestions

8 Correct the mistakes.
1 What to about dinner tomorrow night?
  What about dinner tomorrow night?
2 How to a game of tennis?
  _____ ?
3 What about eat out tonight?
  _____ ?
4 How about go cycling?
  _____ ?
5 What about to play chess?
  _____ ?

Vocabulary

9 Match a word or phrase 1–10 to a word or phrase a–j to make a phrase.

1	factory	a)	the theatre
2	write	b)	centre
3	main	c)	exercise
4	go	d)	table
5	do	e)	abroad
6	go to	f)	a meeting
7	coffee	g)	out
8	travel	h)	worker
9	call	i)	reports
10	have	j)	course

10 Choose three possible words or phrases from the box to complete each sentence.

> call centre worker   fun   office   beef
> mirror   go cycling   nurse   school
> play football   ~~August~~   seafood
> wardrobe   lamb   go to the theatre
> sofa   boring   ~~February~~   hospital
> waiter   ~~September~~   exciting

1 My birthday is in *August / February / September*.
2 I am a _____ .
3 I never eat _____ .
4 The party was really _____ .
5 Have you got a _____ in your bedroom?
6 Do you often _____ ?
7 I work in a/an _____ .

Vocabulary | saying years

1 Correct the phrases in the 'say' column.

Write	Say	
1 1982	nineteen and eighty-two	✗
	nineteen eighty-two	✓
2 2004	two hundred and four	✗
	_____	✓
3 1803	eighteen zero three	✗
	_____	✓
4 1909	nineteen hundred and nine	✗
	_____	✓
5 1970	nineteen seventeen	✗
	_____	✓

2 **a** `9.1` Cover the tapescript below. Listen and write the dates next to each picture.

1
1st July, 1941
ten seconds
long, $9

2
_____
_____

3
_____
_____

4
_____
_____

TAPESCRIPT

1 The first TV advert was on 1st July, 1941. It was ten seconds long and the cost was just nine dollars.
2 The first newspaper crossword was on 21st December, 1913. It was called a 'Word-cross'.
3 The first mobile phone call was on 3rd April, 1973. It was in New York.
4 The first tourist in space was on 28th April, 2001. His name was Dennis Tito.

---

b Listen again. Write the extra information.

Grammar | past of *to be*: affirmative

3 Complete the texts with *was* or *were*.

1

Peter Sellers is a British icon. He (1) _was_ born on 8th September, 1925, in Hampshire, the UK. His parents (2) _____ Agnes and Bill Sellers. They (3) _____ actors and singers in the theatre. In the 1950s, Peter Sellers (4) _____ a star of the radio. In the 1960s and 1970s he (5) _____ a film star. *The Pink Panther* and *Dr Strangelove* (6) _____ Peter Sellers' films.

2

The Beatles (1) _____ John, Paul, George and Ringo. They (2) _____ from Liverpool. Their first name (3) _____ *The Quarrymen*. In 1961 they (4) _____ popular in Liverpool and Hamburg. Their first hit, in 1962, (5) _____ *Love Me Do*. Their next song, *Please Please Me*, (6) _____ number one in early 1963. *Revolver* and *Let It Be* (7) _____ Beatles albums.

4 Make these sentences past with *was* or *were*.

1 Jeff and I are late for the party.
2 My son and daughter are at home.
3 I'm a computer engineer.
4 You're my best friend.
5 We're in the garage.
6 Franz is my sister's best friend.
7 This book is really exciting.
8 They're at school today.
9 She's a university lecturer in London.
10 It's my favourite restaurant.

How to ... | talk about childhood

5 Put the words in the correct order to make sentences.

1 good When young, I was actor.
I was a
When I was young, I was a good actor.

2 she was a When beautiful. she was child,

_____ .

3 children, friends. When they they were were

_____ .

4 was young, When he Tim very thin. was

_____ .

5 you were you a child, When were happy?

_____ ?

6 I was wasn't young, good at When I sport.

_____ .

Vocabulary | prepositions

6 Write complete sentences.

1 (Einstein/born/14th March, 1879)
Einstein was born on 14th March, 1879.

2 (Alfred Hitchcock/famous/his films)

_____ .

3 (Margaret Thatcher/friends/Ronald Reagan)

_____ .

4 (Martin Luther King and Spike Lee/born/ Atlanta in Georgia)

_____ .

5 (Marilyn Monroe/married/Joe DiMaggio and Arthur Miller)

_____ .

6 (Lyndon Johnson/President/America/1963 to 1969)

_____ .

7 (Some of Nina Simone's music/similar/Billie Holiday's music)

_____ .

8 (Mikhail Glinka/good/singing)

_____ .

Reading

7 Read the webpage then mark the sentences true (T) or false (F).

1 George Washington was the first president of the US.

2 Samuel Huntington was the President of the US in 1779.

3 A billion in the US and a billion in the UK are the same.

4 John D. Rockerfeller was a billionaire in the UK.

5 The first World Cup was in Argentina.

6 The first World Cup winner was Uruguay.

---

http://www.famousfirsts.com/

More Famous Firsts

You ask the questions, we find the answers!

Who was the first president of the US?

Polly Kitten

Well Polly, most people think it was George Washington but it was Samuel Huntington in 1779. George Washington was the first president with the new constitution in 1789.

Who was the first billionaire?

Phil Smythe

Good question, Phil. A billion is different in the UK and the US. In the US it is 1,000,000,000 (one thousand million). In the UK it is 1,000,000,000,000 (one million million). Anyway, the first billionaire in American money was John D. Rockerfeller in 1916. His company was Standard Oil.

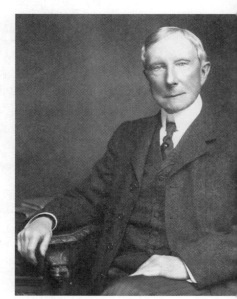

When was the first World Cup?

Marta Diaz

The first World Cup was in 1930 in Uruguay. There were thirteen countries in the competition. Argentina and Uruguay were the two teams in the final. Uruguay were the winners, 4–2.

Grammar | past of *to be*: negatives and questions

1 a Read the profile and complete the sentences.

Cate Blanchett

PROFILE

Name: Catherine Elise Blanchett
Born: 14th May, 1969, in Melbourne, Australia
Father: Robert Blanchett, from the US
Mother: June Blanchett, from Australia
Childhood: good actor at school
University: Melbourn University (Economics)
First big film: *Oscar and Lucinda*
Children: Dashiell (born 2001), Roman (born 2004)

1 (Cate/born/the UK)
Cate wasn't born in the UK .
She was born in Australia .

2 (Her parents/from/the UK)
_____ . _____ .

3 (She/a good singer/at school)
_____ . _____ .

4 (Her subject at university/English)
_____ . _____ .

5 (Her first big film/Elizabeth I)
_____ . _____ .

6 (Her children/born/2002)
_____ . _____ .

b Write questions from the prompts in Ex. 1a.

1 Was Cate born in the UK?
No, she wasn't .

2 _____ ?
_____ .

3 _____ ?
_____ .

4 _____ ?
_____ .

5 _____ ?
_____ .

6 _____ ?
_____ .

2 Complete the conversation with *was, wasn't, were* or *weren't*.

Interviewer: So, Melissa, when you (1) *were* a child, (2) _____ you a good singer?
Melissa: No, I (3) _____ . I (4) _____ a very bad singer.
Interviewer: Who (5) _____ your singing teacher?
Melissa: Her name (6) _____ Mrs Parsons. She (7) _____ great – really great!
Interviewer: Who (8) _____ your favourite singers?
Melissa: Aretha Franklin and Billie Holiday (9) _____ my favourite singers.
Interviewer: (10) _____ your parents singers?
Melissa: No, they (11) _____ . My mother (12) _____ a scientist and my father (13) _____ a househusband.

3 Correct the mistakes.

1 Was you a good singer when you were young?
Were you a good singer when you were young?
2 Richard and Alex isn't at work yesterday.
3 I not a maths teacher. I was a science teacher.
4 Were Ronald Reagan a film star?
5 My father not a composer but he was a musician.
6 Was you at home last night?
7 When were your last holiday?
8 Who your best friend was at school?
9 What were Marlon Brando's last film?
10 Were your father a politician?

Vocabulary | *yesterday, last, ago*

4   **a** Read the text. Put the pictures in time order.

My name is Emily Barnes. I work for Trans-Global Software. I travel abroad a lot. For example, last week I was in Moscow. Three days ago I was in Athens. Fifteen days ago I was in New York. Yesterday I was in London. Last month I was in Paris.

A

B

C

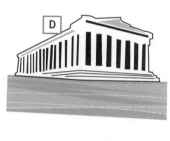
D

E

b Complete the phrases with *yesterday, ago* or *last*.

Today is Wednesday 24th March, 2008

1   23rd March, evening = *yesterday* evening
2   17th March = _____ _____ _____
3   2007 = _____ _____
4   23rd March/24th March, night = _____ night
5   Monday 15th March – Sunday 21st March = _____ _____
6   14th March = ten _____ _____
7   February 2008 = _____ _____
8   23rd March, morning = _____ _____

Listening

5   **a** **9.2** Cover the tapescript and listen. Answer the questions below.

1   What does Marianne want?
2   Where is The Coffee Palace?
3   What was Marianne's last job?
4   What is Favourite Fashions?
5   What was Marianne's first job after high school?
6   Can she make good coffee?

b Listen again. Complete the tapescript.

> **TAPESCRIPT**
>
> **A:** Hello. Are you Mr Sarandon?
> **B:** Yes, that's (1) *right* .
> **A:** I'm Marianne. Nice to meet you.
> **B:** Hello, Marianne. Nice to meet you, too. Please, sit down. (2) _____ you like a coffee?
> **A:** No, thank you.
> **B:** So, you want a job in The Coffee Palace.
> **A:** Yes, that's right.
> **B:** What (3) _____ your last job?
> **A:** I was a sales assistant in a clothes shop.
> **B:** Was that here in Chicago?
> **A:** No, it (4) _____ . It was in San Diego. I'm from California.
> **B:** I see. What was the name of the shop?
> **A:** Favourite Fashions.
> **B:** Was (5) _____ your first job after high school?
> **A:** No, it wasn't. My first job was in a call centre. Then I was a PA in an office but that (6) _____ very interesting.
> **B:** OK. Can you make good coffee?
> **A:** I can make great coffee …

Vocabulary | housework

1 a Choose the correct word to complete each phrase.

1 *cook/iron/wash* dinner
2 *wash/clean/do* the laundry
3 *iron/vacuum/cook* the house
4 *cook/wash/clean* the bathroom
5 *iron/cook/vacuum* a shirt
6 *cook/iron/wash* the dishes

b Write a phrase above next to each picture below.

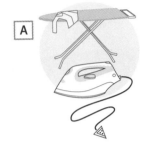

A

B

C

D

E

F

c Write a suggestion in each space below. Use *Could you ...?* and a phrase from Ex. 1a.

1 A: *Could you iron my shirts*?
   B: Sorry, I can't. The iron is broken.
2 A: _____ ?
   B: Sorry, I can't. The washing machine is broken.
3 A: _____ ?
   B: Sure. What would you like to eat?
4 A: _____ ?
   B: Yes, OK. Where's the vacuum cleaner?
5 A: _____ ?
   B: I can't. The kitchen sink is broken.
6 A: _____ ?
   B: I can't. My brother is having a shower!

How to ... | ask about an experience

2 Match a question from the box to an answer.

> How was the flight?
> How was your weekend?
> How was your holiday?
> How was school?
> How was the party?

1 A: _____
   B: It was OK, but the flight attendants weren't very nice.
2 A: _____
   B: It was good. My teacher likes me!
3 A: _____
   B: It was great. There were fifty people there.
4 A: _____
   B: Fine, thanks. I was in town on Saturday and I was at home on Sunday.
5 A: _____
   B: It was great. The weather was lovely and the food was very nice.

Grammar | *Can/Could you ...? Can/Could I ...?*

3 Put the words in the correct order to make requests/ask for permission.

1 you? I to Can talk
   Can I talk to you?
2 you dinner? Can cook
   _____ ?
3 the Could open you window?
   _____ ?
4 down? I Can sit
   _____ ?
5 home at work I tomorrow? Could
   _____ ?
6 on television? Could turn you the
   _____ ?

4 Match a conversation to a picture.

1 **A:** Could you carry my suitcase?
B: Of course.

2 **A:** Can I use your phone?
B: Yes, you can.

3 **A:** Could I have a cup of tea?
B: Yes, of course.

4 **A:** Could you take a photo of us?
B: Yes, sure.

5 **A:** Could you answer the phone?
B: Yes, OK.

a

b

c

d

e

Writing

5 Read the letter. There are nine mistakes. Find them and correct them.

Dear Tesia,

Long time ~~not~~ *no* see. How are you? Thanks for your last letter. How were your holiday? Our holiday wasn't very good. The hotel was awful and the weather is very bad.

My family fine, thank you. Viktor is four and Roza is two year old now. I've got a new job. Last year I'm a sales rep. but now I'm a sales manager. The new job is exciting but I work long hours.

There is a conference in your city next Thursday. I could stay at your house on Wednesday night? I can stay in a hotel but I want see you.

Could send me an email or call me this week?

Love,

Joanna

Vocabulary | good and bad experiences

1 a Read the sentences. Write the missing verbs in the puzzle. What is the hidden phrase?

1 You _meet_ a famous person.
2 A thief _____ your mobile phone.
3 You _____ to a new house.
4 You _____ in bed all day.
5 A police officer _____ you.
6 You _____ your leg.
7 You _____ the lottery.
8 You _____ your wallet or purse.
9 You _____ some money on the street.

hidden phrase

(crossword puzzle with starting letter g)

b Match a phrase in Ex. 1a to a picture below.

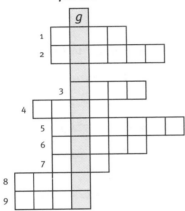

you break your leg

_____

_____

_____

_____

_____

Grammar 1 | Past Simple: affirmative

2 Complete the email with a verb from the box in the Past Simple.

> walk   want   cook   ~~start~~   listen   live
> play   move   close   talk

to: lydia.fernandez@fastmail.com
from: riena_miller@epost.co.uk

Hello Lydia,

How are you? The weather here in Madrid is great. Our day (1) _started_ at 7.30a.m. yesterday! Consuela (2) _____ breakfast for us. Then we (3) _____ to the Prado Gallery. Felipe (4) _____ to see the paintings by Goya and Velazquez. Felipe (5) _____ in Madrid when he was a child but he (6) _____ to the UK when he was 8 years old.

After lunch we (7) _____ tennis in the park. The park (8) _____ at 5.00p.m. In the evening we (9) _____ to music and (10) _____ about our favourite singers at Consuela's house.

That's all for now. Send me an email and tell me your news!

Love,

Reina

Pronunciation | /t/, /d/ and /ɪd/

3 Write /t/, /d/ or /ɪd/ next to the *-ed* ending of each verb.

1 wanted _/ɪd/_
2 liked _/t/_
3 moved _/d/_
4 talked _____
5 wanted _____
6 closed _____
7 arrested _____
8 listened _____
9 asked _____
10 finished _____
11 played _____
12 cooked _____

Grammar 2 | Past Simple: negatives and questions

4   **a** Complete the text with the correct form of the verbs in brackets.

Van Gogh's early life

Van Gogh (1) _____ (be) born in The Hague in Holland in 1853. In 1869 he (2)_____ (start) work. His company, Goupil & Cie, was from Paris. Van Gogh (3) _____ (not move) to Paris but he (4) _____ (not stay) in The Hague. In 1873 he (5) _____ (move) to London. He (6) _____ (love) a woman called Eugenie Loyer but she (7) _____ (not love) him. Van Gogh was very unhappy. He (8) _____ (not like) his job and in 1874 he moved to Paris. But Van Gogh (9) _____ (not stay) in Paris ...

b Write questions and answers about Van Gogh.

1   (Van Gogh/stay/Paris?)
    A: *Did Van Gogh stay in Paris*?
    B: *No, he didn't*.

2   (Van Gogh/move/London?)
    A: _____ ?
    B: Yes, _____ .

3   (Van Gogh/love/Eugenie Loyer?)
    A: _____ ?
    B: Yes, _____ .

4   (Eugenie Loyer/love/Van Gogh?)
    A: _____ ?
    B: No, _____ .

5   (Van Gogh/like/his job?)
    A: _____ ?
    B: No, _____ .

Listening

5   `10.1` Cover the tapescript below and listen. Match the events 1–6 to the dates a–f.

Events		Dates	
1	Gauguin was born	a)	1855
2	Gauguin moved to Peru	b)	1903
3	Gauguin moved back to France	c)	1888
4	Gauguin lived with Van Gogh	d)	1895
5	Gauguin moved to Tahiti	e)	1848
6	Gauguin died	f)	1849

TAPESCRIPT

A: This is a painting by Paul Gauguin. His full name was Eugene Henri Paul Gauguin. He was born in Paris on 7th June, 1848. His family moved to Peru in 1849.

B: Did they stay in Peru?

A: No, they didn't. In 1855 Gauguin moved back to France with his mother.

B: Was he friends with Van Gogh?

A: An interesting question. He lived with Van Gogh for three months in 1888 but Gauguin didn't like Van Gogh and he didn't like Van Gogh's paintings.

B: When did Gauguin move to Tahiti?

A: He moved there in 1895. His wife and children stayed in Europe. Gauguin didn't want to live in Europe and he loved art from other countries. He worked in Tahiti but it wasn't easy. He wasn't rich, he was very ill and the police in Tahiti even arrested him! He died in 1903.

Grammar | Past Simple: irregular verbs

1 **a** Complete the sentences with the Past Simple of the verb in brackets.

1 My brother *got married* (get married) last year.
2 Oliver and Emma _____ (buy) a house in Spain.
3 We _____ (go) to the cinema last night.
4 You _____ (see) her. She was at the party.
5 Rachel _____ (say) no.
6 My manager and my wife _____ (meet) your daughter yesterday.
7 He _____ (give) an awful presentation yesterday.
8 Irena and I _____ (find) a beautiful hotel in the centre of Prague.

b Complete the puzzle with the past simple of the verbs below. Some are regular and some are irregular. Find the hidden phrase.

1 play	7 buy
2 win	8 find
3 lose	9 finish
4 say	10 listen
5 come	11 meet
6 go	

hidden phrase

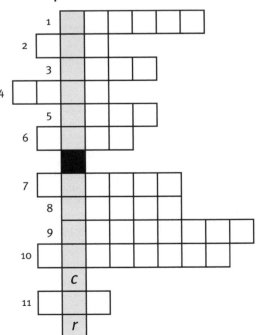

c Complete the text with the correct form of the verb in brackets.

Newly-weds win €15million in Euro Lottery

Janice and Derek Parker from Cornwall (1) _____ (win) €15 million in the Euro Lottery last week. Janice and Derek (2) _____ (get married) on Saturday morning. 'We (3) _____ (not go) on holiday,' (4) _____ (say) Janice. 'We (5) _____ (not have) any money. But we (6) _____ (go) to a nice restaurant. In the evening I (7) _____ (look) at the lottery numbers and I (8) _____ (be) so happy'. And last Friday Derek (9) _____ (buy) a present for Janice. What (10) _____ (he/buy) for her? He (11) _____ (not buy) a new car or a new house. He (12) _____ (buy) a new washing machine for her!

d Put the words in the correct order to make questions.

1 find you your Did wallet?
Did you find your wallet?
2 Terry go out night? Did last
_____?
3 car? they Did a buy new
_____?
4 her? Did love you
_____?
5 to Harry London? Did move
_____?
6 say 'Yes'? Did you
_____?
7 lose passport you on Did holiday? your
_____?
8 Did lottery? win we the
_____?

Vocabulary | high numbers

2 Write the numbers.

1   2,150 – _two thousand_, _one hundred_ and _fifty_

2   1,010 – _____ _____ and _____

3   980 – _____ _____ and _____

4   15,612 – _____ _____ , _____ _____ and _____

5   9,999 – _____ _____ , _____ _____ and _____-_____

6   86,321 - _____-_____ _____ , _____ _____ and _____-_____

7   115,200 - _____ _____ and _____ _____ , _____ _____

8   200,109 – _____ _____ _____ , _____ _____ and _____

Listening

3 **10.2** Listen and write the numbers in the interesting facts below.

Interesting facts

1   Mount Everest is _8,850_ metres tall.

2   There are more than _____ countries in the world.

3   About _____ people live in the Vatican City.

4   The River Nile in Egypt is _____ kilometres long.

5   Jean Calment died in 1997. She was _____ years old.

6   There are about _____ million cars in the world.

7   There are about _____ pandas in China.

8   There are between _____ and _____ languages in the world.

9   The Pacific Ocean is about _____ million square kilometres.

10 The average person has between _____ and _____ hairs on their head.

Writing

4 Rewrite the sentences in the correct order to make news stories.

News story 1

A   He got married to Alexandre Serrano on his eighty-first birthday.

B   'Rio was very beautiful,' he said, 'but Alexandre is very, very beautiful.'

C   He met her on holiday in Rio de Janeiro.

D   It was a good week for Cristiano Andrade from Portugal.

1   _It was a good week for Cristiano Andrade from Portugal._

2   _____ .

3   _____ .

4   _____ .

News story 2

A   Now he can't play football for six months.

B   They bought footballer Clive Lightfoot for £1.6 million.

C   Clive arrived at the football club on Monday morning.

D   It was a bad week for football team Rochdale United.

E   In the afternoon he broke his leg.

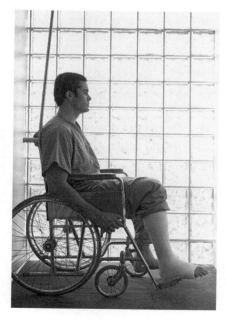

1   _____ .

2   _____ .

3   _____ .

4   _____ .

5   _____ .

Grammar | *going to*

1   Read the sentences below and write another sentence. Use the verbs in the box and *going to*.

> find a new job   ~~get married~~
> go to the beach   go to bed
> break your leg   be rich
> move to a hot country
> cook dinner tonight

1   Rachel and Steven are in love.
    They*'re going to get married*.
2   This country is cold. I _____ .
3   I went to bed late last night. I _____ early tonight.
4   Estelle doesn't like her job. She _____ .
5   We are on holiday. We _____ this afternoon.
6   You can't ski. You _____ .
7   He's a good businessman. He _____ .
8   She's a great chef. _____ .

2   **a** Look at the chart below. Write two sentences for each person/people.

Winona and her family: plans for next year		
	going to	not going to
me	eat a lot of vegetables	eat meat
my husband	do a lot of exercise	surf the Internet every evening
me and my husband	move house	watch a lot of TV
my sister	get a new job	go out every night
my parents	travel abroad	buy a new car

1   *I'm going to eat a lot of vegetables.*
    I'm not going to eat meat.
2   He _____ .
    _____ .
3   We _____ .
    _____ .
4   She _____ .
    _____ .
5   They _____ .
    _____ .

b   Write questions for Winona and her family.

1   (you/eat meat)
    Are you going to eat meat?
    No, I'm not.
2   (your sister/get a new job)
    Is your sister going to get a new job?
    Yes, she is.
3   (your parents/buy a new car)
    _____ ?
    No, they're not.
4   (your husband/surf the Internet every evening)
    _____ ?
    No, he's not.
5   (Where/you and your husband/move to)
    _____ ?
    A big house near his parents.
6   (What job/your sister/get)
    _____ ?
    She's going to be a PA.
7   (Where/your parents/travel to)
    _____ ?
    They're going to travel to Japan and Korea.
8   (What exercise/you and your husband/do)
    _____ ?
    We're going to go cycling.

Listening

3   **10.3** Listen and write the questions.

1   A: *What are you going to do next weekend*?
    B: Nothing. Why?
2   A: _____ ?
    B: Yes, I am.
3   A: _____ ?
    B: Because they want to live in Spain.
4   A: _____ ?
    B: No, he isn't. He's going to take the bus.
5   A: _____ ?
    B: You are.
6   A: _____ ?
    B: No, we aren't. We haven't got any money.
7   A: _____ ?
    B: In the centre of town.
8   A: _____ ?
    B: He's going to get a new job.

Vocabulary | future plans

4   **a** Match a verb 1–6 with the words a–f to make a phrase.

1 learn	a)	to university
2 have	b)	a business
3 start	c)	-----
4 get	d)	to drive
5 retire	e)	a child
6 go	f)	fit

b Look at the pictures. What are these people going to do? Use a phrase from Ex. 4a and *going to*.

1

He's going to learn to drive.

2

_____ .

3

_____ .

4

_____ .

5

_____ .

6

_____ .

Reading

5   **a** Read the article below and complete the information about Alex.

Name: *Alex* _____
Age: _____
Alex's website: _____

The million-dollar idea

ALEX TEW was 21-years old and he was poor. He was a university student from the UK but he didn't have any money. So what did he do? He had an idea – a million-dollar idea. Now he's a millionaire university student.

Alex's idea was simple. He bought a website: www.milliondollarhomepage.com. There were one million pixels on Alex's website (pixels are small dots of colour). Alex sold each pixel for $1. Big and small companies bought pixels on Million Dollar Home Page. For example, The Times, a newspaper, bought 2,800 pixels. When you click on these pixels, you go to *The Times* website.

Alex started the business on 5th August, 2005. In the first four weeks he sold 300,000 pixels. On 11th January, 2006, a company bought the last 1,000 pixels. Alex was a millionaire.

So what is Alex going to do next? He's going to finish his university course. Then he's going to start new Internet businesses. For Alex, business is fun and making one million dollars is easy!

b Read the article again and answer the questions.

1 What was Alex's problem?
2 What does Alex do now?
3 What did Alex buy?
4 How much was each pixel on Alex's website?
5 When did Alex start the business?
6 When did Alex make $1,000,000?
7 What are Alex's plans?

past of *to be*

1 Complete the conversation with the correct form of the Past of *to be*.

A: ... and now we've got a famous person in the studio. Please welcome, Roxanne Hewitt.

B: Thank you.

A: So Roxanne, where (1) *were* you born?

B: I (2) _____ born in Timisoara in Romania.

A: You're a famous actor now but (3) _____ you an actor when you (4) _____ young?

B: Yes, I (5) _____ . My first job as an actor (6) _____ when I (7) _____ eight years old.

A: Eight years old? (8) _____ it a film?

B: No, it (9) _____ . It (10) _____ a TV show.

A: (11) _____ your parents actors?

B: No, they (12) _____ . My mother (13) _____ a university lecturer and my father (14) _____ a factory worker. In their leisure time they (15) _____ singers and dancers but they (16) _____ very good. Sorry mum and dad!

2 Write questions with the past of *to be*.

1 (Where/he born?)
Where was he born?

2 (What/their names?)
_____ ?

3 (When/you a teacher?)
_____ ?

4 (Where/she yesterday?)
_____ ?

5 (When/your birthday?)
_____ ?

6 (How/your holiday?)
_____ ?

Can I/you; Could I/you

3 Complete the questions with *I* or *you*.

1 Can *you* spell that, please?

2 Could _____ use your computer?

3 Could _____ open the door for me?

4 Can _____ help you?

5 Could _____ listen to your Billie Holiday CD?

6 Can _____ sing me a song?

7 Can _____ ask you a question?

8 Could _____ cook tonight? I don't want to.

Past simple

4 Complete the sentences with a verb from the box in the Past simple.

> say ~~arrest~~ get come play lose

1 The police *arrested* the art thief in the gallery.

2 Louise _____ home at 12 o'clock last night.

3 I _____ my wallet last week. There was €30 and my credit cards in it.

4 I talked to my boss about a 3-week holiday but he _____ no.

5 I went to bed late last night and I _____ up late this morning.

6 Danny and Nina _____ tennis yesterday.

5 Complete the conversations with the Past Simple of the verb in brackets.

1 A: When *did* the match *start*? (start)
B: It *started* at half past three.

2 A: What _____ you _____ for lunch? (have)
B: I _____ salad.

3 A: Where _____ they _____ to? (move)
B: They _____ to Australia but they _____ _____ to Sydney.

4 A: _____ you _____ swimming? (go)
B: We _____ _____ swimming. We _____ to the park.

5 A: What _____ you _____ in town? (buy)
B: I _____ some clothes.

6 A: _____ Marlene _____ any photos of you. (take)
B: No, she _____ But she _____ some pictures of Michael.

7 A: Where _____ Harry and Sally _____ ? (meet)
B: They _____ at university.

8 A: Where _____ you _____ her? (see)
B: I _____ her in a café on Upper Street.

going to

6 Write complete sentences with the correct form of *going to*.

1 (Terry/get married)
Terry's going to get married.

2 (I/not live abroad)
I'm not going to live abroad.

3 (Samuel/learn to dance)
_____ .

4 (Art and Garfunkel/not make a new record)
_____ .

5 (We/move to Scotland)
_____ ?

6 (The police/arrest him)
_____ .

7 (Mike and Danielle/not come to the wedding)
_____ .

8 (He/not cook dinner)
_____ ?

7 Write questions to find the missing information.

1 They're going to move to *?*.
Where are they going to move to?

2 He's going to buy *?*.
_____ ?

3 I'm going to talk to *?*.
_____ ?

4 We're going to meet them at *?* o'clock.
_____ ?

5 They're going to play *?*.
_____ ?

6 He's going to have *?* for dinner.
_____ ?

7 I'm going to retire when I'm *?* years old?
_____ ?

8 She's going to learn to *?*.
_____ ?

Vocabulary

8 Write the numbers in full.

1 10,301
ten thousand, three hundred and one

2 733
_____

3 1,140
_____

4 66,000
_____

5 112,500
_____

6 101
_____

7 199,999
_____

8 500,005
_____

9 Complete each phrase with a verb from the box.

> move   go   ~~break~~   learn   win   get (x2)
> have   start   stay

1 *break* your leg
2 _____ to university
3 _____ children
4 _____ married
5 _____ a business
6 _____ the lottery
7 _____ to a new country
8 _____ to swim
9 _____ in bed
10 _____ fit

Answer key

Unit 1 Arrivals

Lesson 1.1
Speaking
1a **1** Nice, too **2** Hi **3** Welcome, Thank **4** name, I'm
b A 2 **B** 1 **C** 4 **D** 3

Vocabulary: numbers 0–9
2

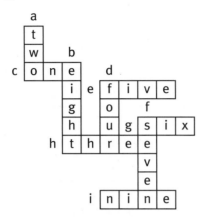

Listening
3 **1** 438 **2** 107 **3** 925 **4** 619 **5** 843 **6** 702

Grammar: I'm/you're
4 **1 A:** Hello. Welcome *to Linton Hotel*.
B: Thank you. *I'm David Franks*.
A: *You're in room 601*, Mr Franks.

2 A: Hello. Welcome *to Grange Hotel.*
B: Thank you. *I'm Susan Jacks*.
A: *You're in room 329*, Ms Jacks.

3 A: Hello. Welcome *to Opera Hotel.*
B: Thank you. *I'm Ricardo Mendoza.*
A: *You're in room 540*, Mr Mendoza.

5 **1 A:** Hello. I̶ Svetlana Rochev. I'm
2 A: Good morning, Mr Nakamura. Y̶o̶u̶ in room 922. You're
3 A: Hello. I̶m̶ Jin Chang. I'm
B: I̶m̶ Farah Coleman. I'm
B: Hello, Mr Wilson. Y̶o̶u̶r̶e̶ in room 102. You're

Vocabulary: greetings
6 **07.30 Henry:** Good morning, Ms Sharapova.
Maria Sharapova: Good morning, Henry.
15.30 Henry: Good afternoon, Mr Geldof.
Bob Geldof: Good afternoon, Henry.
19.30 Henry: Good evening, Gwyneth.
Gwyneth Paltrow: Good evening, Henry.
23.00 Henry: Good night, Jamie.
Jamie Foxx: Good night, Henry.

7
Evan: Good morning. **Polly:** Good morning. **Evan:** I'm Evan Larson.
Polly: I'm Polly Tiller. **Evan:** Nice to meet you. **Polly:** Nice to meet you, too.

Lesson 1.2
Vocabulary: letters a–z
1a **a** 1 **b** 2 **c** 2 **d** 2 **e** 2 **f** 3 **g** 2 **h** 1 **i** 4 **j** 1 **k** 1
l 3 **m** 3 **n** 3 **o** 5 **p** 2 **q** 6 **r** 7 **s** 3 **t** 2 **u** 6 **v** 2
w 6 **x** 3 **y** 4 **z** 3

Vocabulary: countries
2a **1** Italy **2** Poland **3** Mexico **4** Turkey **5** Spain
6 Russia **7** Argentina **8** Brazil

b **1** Japan **2** Australia **3** Argentina **4** The UK **5** Germany
6 India **7** Brazil Hidden country = Portugal

Grammar: he's, she's, it's
3 **1** He's Sergio. **2** She's Francesca. **3** It's London.
4 She's Amy. **5** It's New York. **6** He's Calvin.

4 **1** He's from Brazil. He's in the US. **2** She's from India. She's in the UK. **3** He's from Argentina. He's in Japan. **4** He's from the US. He's in Australia. **5** She's from Germany. She's in India. **6** She's from the UK. She's in Argentina.

Reading
5
1 Name: Marsha Rees. **From:** the US. **2 Name:** Paul Earle. Room: 891 **3 Name:** Candy Banks. Room: 614

Lesson 1.3
1a **1** Sorry. **2** Pardon? **3** No, thank you. **4** Nice to meet you. **5** Excuse me. **6** Yes, please.
b **a** Excuse me. **b** Nice to meet you. **c** Pardon? **d** Sorry. **e** No, thank you. **f** Yes, please.

How to ... introduce people
2 **1 You:** Nicole, this is Keith. **Nicole:** Nice to meet you, Keith. **Keith:** Nice to meet you too, Nicole. **2 You:** Colin, this is Laura. **Colin:** Nice to meet you, Laura. **Laura:** Nice to meet you too, Colin. **3 You** Harry. This is Mary. **Harry:** Nice to meet you, Mary. **Mary:** Nice to meet you too, Harry.

Grammar: Where are you from?
3 **Theo:** Carol, this is Ali. **Carol:** Nice to meet you. **Ali:** Nice to meet you, too. **Carol:** Where are you from, Ali? **Ali:** I'm from the UK. **Carol:** Where are you from in the UK? **Ali:** I'm from London.

4 **1** are, from **2** Where are **3** you from **4** you from, from **5** Where, from **6** are, from, I'm

5 **1 You:** Where are you from in Italy? **Isabella:** I'm from Rome. **2 You:** Where are you from? **Shah:** I'm from India. **3 You:** Where are you from? **Fabiana:** I'm from Argentina. **4 You:** Where are you from in Mexico? **Gael:** I'm from Guadalajara.

Listening
6 **1 Name:** Stan Allman. From: Brighton (city). **From:** the UK (country). **2 Name:** Nadine Strong. From: Dallas (city). **From:** the US (country). **3 Name:** Chris Hall. From: Victoria (city). **From:** Canada (country).

Unit 2 My life

Lesson 2.1
Vocabulary: family members
1 **1** father – son **2** husband – wife **3** sister – brother **4** mother – daughter **5** son – mother **6** daughter – father

Vocabulary: my life
2 **1** phone **2** address **3** website **4** first name **5** photo **6** mobile phone **7** surname **8** computer hidden word – passport

Vocabulary: numbers 10–99
3 **1** f **2** d **3** e **4** j **5** a **6** c **7** b **8** i **9** g **10** h
4 **1** thirty-two, sixty-four **2** fifty-five, sixty-six **3** fifty, forty **4** twelve, eleven **5** seventy-seven, eighty-four **6** fifty-four, sixty-three **7** sixty-four, eighty-one **8** seventy, thirty

Grammar: Who ...?; my
5 **1** Who's **2** husband **3** she **4** my **5** father **6** Who's **7** son **8** my **9** Who's **10** mother **11** he **12** He's
6 Eduardo 72 Annika 67 Enzo 29 Rozalia 36 Donata 41 Andrew 44 Nico 12 Fulvia 8

74

Reading

7 **Name:** Darren Southgate. **Age:** 57. **From:** Edinburgh in Scotland. **Relationship to David:** father. **Name:** Devandra Branley. **Age:** 35 years old. **From:** San Diego in the US. **Relationship to David:** friend. **Name:** Beverley Wolcott. **Age:** 37 years old. **From:** Dominica in the Caribbean. **Relationship to David:** friend. **Name:** Pauline Southgate. **Age:** 60 years old. **From:** York in the UK. **Relationship to David:** mother.

Lesson 2.2
Vocabulary: Expressions

1 **1** good **2** awful **3** great **4** OK **5** bad

2 **1** She's good. **2** He's OK. **3** She's great. **4** He's bad. **5** She's awful.

3 **1** What's your name? My name's Fadil Husni. **2** What's your address? It's 93 Al Orouba Street, Cairo. **3** What's your phone number? It's 02366 48381. **4** What's your mobile phone number? It's 08112 828344.

4 **1** Who's she? **2** How old are you? **3** What's your name? **4** What's your phone number? **5** How old is he? **6** How do you spell that, please? **7** Where are you from? **8** What's your address? **9** Who's Preston? **10** Where's she from?

5 **Conversation A:** **1** Welcome to Hatson Hotel. **2** What's you name, please? **3** I'm Olivia Dukakis. **4** How do you spell that please. **5** You're in room 815.
Conversation B: **1** What's **your** name, please? **2** How do you spell **that**, please? **3** **What's** your address? **4** **How** do you spell Tavistock? **5** And what's your phone **number**?

Listening

6 **First name:** Brett. **Surname:** Ellis. **Address:** 33 Peel Street, Newcastle. **Phone number:** 00 44 191202149

7 **1** Are you from Poland? **2** My mobile number is 07060 987 885. Please phone! **3** How old are you? **4** What's your name? **5** It's great!

Lesson 2.3
Vocabulary: jobs

1 **1** manager **2** teacher **3** student **4** accountant **5** sales assistant **6** police officer **7** doctor **8** artist **9** engineer **10** actor

2 **Down** **1** police officer **2** artist **6** student **8** doctor **Across** **3** manager **4** actor **5** teacher **7** accountant **9** engineer **10** sales assistant

Grammar 1: a/an

3 **1** He's a police officer. **2** She's an artist. **3** She's a manager. **4** He's/She's an actor. **5** She's a teacher. **6** She's a doctor. **7** He's an accountant. **8** She's a student. **9** She's an engineer. **10** She's a sales assistant.

4 **1** b **2** c **3** f **4** e **5** a **6** d

Grammar 2: his/her

5 **1** He's **2** He's **3** He's **4** His **5** She's **6** She's **7** She's **8** She's **9** She's **10** Her **11** He's **12** He's

6 **1** his **2** His **3** he **4** He's **5** he **6** He's **7** his **8** He's **9** his **10** It's **11** her **12** Her **13** she **14** She's **15** she **16** She's **17** her **18** She's **19** her **20** It's

Reading

7 **1** Name: Derek. Age: 65. Job: doctor. **2** Name: Patricia. Age: 68. Job: teacher. **3** Name: Marie. Age: 38. Job: manager. **4** Name: Sam. Age: 45. Job: engineer. **5** Name: Monica. Age: 44. Job: accountant. **6** Name: Malcolm. Age: 12. Job: student. **7** Name: Debbie. Age: 11. Job: student.

Vocabulary: favourites

8 **1** What's your favourite city? **2** What's your favourite restaurant? **3** Who's your favourite singer? **4** What's your favourite film? **5** What's your favourite book? **6** What's your favourite CD? **7** Who's your favourite actor?

Review and consolidation units 1–2

Grammar: Verb *to be* with *I, you, he, she, it*

1 **1** is **2** am **3** is **4** are **5** am **6** is **7** are **8** is **9** am **10** is

2 **1** She's Mrs Grant. **2** It's a great CD. **3** You're my favourite teacher. **4** I'm Mr Brown. **5** He's from New York. **6** Colette's a student. **7** Peter's in China. **8** You're 21 years old. **9** I'm in Hotel Fernando. **10** It's my favourite film.

my, your, his, her

3 **1** His **2** Its **3** My **4** your **5** Her **6** My **7** Its **8** His **9** Your **10** Her

Where, Who, What, How

4 **1** j **2** e **3** b **4** d **5** h **6** a **7** g **8** c **9** i **10** f

a/an

5 **1** – **2** a **3** an **4** – **5** a **6** a **7** – **8** – **9** an **10** –

Numbers 0–99

6 **1** e **2** f **3** d **4** b **5** h **6** j **7** a **8** i **9** g **10** c

7 **1** twenty-five **2** eighteen **3** fifty **4** thirty-one **5** twelve **6** ninety-nine **7** forty-four **8** fourteen **9** eighty-two **10** sixty-seven

Vocabulary

8 **1, 6, 10** = jobs **2, 8, 12** = family **3, 4, 9** = adjectives **5, 7, 11** = numbers

9 **1** singer **2** address **3** Excuse **4** assistant **5** passport **6** website **7** sixty **8** favourite **9** Nice **10** officer

Unit 3 Travel

Lesson 3.1
Vocabulary: tourist attractions

1 **1** castle **2** mountain **3** cathedral **4** museum **5** market **6** gallery **7** palace **8** lake

2 **a** cathedral **b** palace **c** gallery **d** lake **e** market **f** castle **g** museum **h** mountain

Vocabulary: adjectives

3 **1** old – modern **2** ugly – beautiful **3** small – big

4 **A** old, beautiful **B** small, modern **C** big, ugly **D** small, beautiful **E** old, big **F** big, modern

Grammar: the verb *to be* with *we* and *they*; *our* and *their*

5 **1** We're **2** Their **3** They're **4** Our **5** They're **6** Our **7** their **8** we're

6 **1** We're **2** Our **3** We're **4** They're **5** our **6** their **7** their

7 **1** Their, Our **2** We're, They're **3** Their, Our **4** We're, They're **5** Their, Our

Writing

8 **1** c **2** f **3** e **4** a **5** b **6** d

Lesson 3.2
Vocabulary: holiday things

1 **1** a camera **D** **2** a top **H** **3** a backpack **B** **4** a pair of trousers **J** **5** a book **F** **6** a skirt **I** **7** a pair of shoes **C** **8** a suitcase **E** **9** a map **A** **10** an MP3 player **G**

2a, b **a** two CDs /z/ **b** two passports /s/ **c** two computers /z/ **d** four suitcases /ɪz/ **e** two maps /s/ **f** two books /s/ **g** three mobile phones /z/ **h** two pairs of shoes /z/ **j** three tops /s/

3 **1** Our cameras are in the suitcase. **2** They're accountants. **3** Where are our backpacks? **4** Who are your favourite singers? **5** Their maps are awful. **6** They're great MP3 players. **7** Our favourite pairs of shoes are very old. **8** How old are their daughters?

Grammar: the verb *to be*: negative

4 **1** He isn't my brother.   **2** You're not 21 years old.   **3** It's not/It isn't my camera.   **4** Ronnie and Nicky aren't friends.   **5** London's not/isn't my favourite city.   **6** We're not students.   **7** I'm not a good actor.   **8** Simone's not/isn't from Italy.   **9** Will and I aren't her teachers.   **10** I'm not very old.

5 **1** You're not a teacher. You're a student.   **2** It's not a skirt. It's a pair of trousers.   **3** We're not from the US. We're from the UK.   **4** Vienna isn't my favourite country. It's my favourite city.   **5** He's not/isn't my sister. He's my brother.   **6** I'm not fifteen. I'm fifty.   **7** They're not open today. They're closed.   **8** She's not/isn't an accountant. She's an engineer.

Listening

6 **1** F   **2** F   **3** F   **4** T   **5** F   **6** T   **7** T   **8** F   **9** F

7 **1** The teacher is Peter Keef.   **2** Celia Cruz isn't the sister of Penelope Cruz.   **3** Penelope Cruz is from Madrid in Spain.   **4** (T)   **5** Raymond Petit is the husband of Catherine Petit.   **6** (T)   **7** (T)   **8** Catherine is twenty-eight years old.   **9** The teacher is 41 years old.

Lesson 3.3
Vocabulary: days of the week

1 Monday Tuesday Wednesday Thursday Friday Saturday Sunday

How to … use *here* and *there*

2 **1** b   **2** a   **3** b   **4** a

Grammar: Yes/No questions with *to be*

3 **1** Are   **2** are   **3** Is   **4** it   **5** Is   **6** is   **7** It's   **8** is   **9** Are   **10** are   **11** Are   **12** they   **13** aren't   **14** Is   **15** Yes   **16** is   **17** this   **18** it   **19** is

Conversation 1 = **C**
Conversation 2 = **B**
Conversation 3 = **A**

4 **1** Is she a good singer?   **2** Is it a big museum?   **3** Is he a new friend?   **4** Are they beautiful lakes?   **5** Are you a good actor?   **6** Are they small cities?

5 **1** open   **2** Yes, it is   **3** Is it   **4** No, it isn't   **5** Is it   **6** Yes, it is   **7** Is it   **8** it is

Reading

6 Picture 1 Dracula's Castle   Picture 2 New York's Museum of Contemporary Art   Picture 3 Lake Baikal

7 **1** Yes, it is.   **2** No, it isn't. It's in Siberia.   **3** No, it isn't. It's big.   **4** Yes, it is.   **5** No, it isn't. It's in the US.   **6** No, it isn't. It's modern.   **7** Yes, it is.   **8** No, it isn't.   **9** Yes, it is.   **10** No, it isn't. It's near Brasov.   **11** No, it isn't.   **12** No, it isn't.

Unit 4 In town

Lesson 4.1
Vocabulary: places in town

1

UK city

1	m	a	r	k	e	t		
2	c	a	f	e				
3 b	a	n	k					
4	c	h	e	m	i	s	t	
5 c	a	s	h	p	o	i	n	t
6 c	i	n	e	m	a			
7	s	u	p	e	t	m	a	r	k	e	t
8 r	e	s	t	a	u	r	a	n	t
9	n	e	w	s	a	g	e	n	t
10 c	a	r		p	a	r	k

Vocabulary: food and drink

2 **1** **a** Chicken sandwich   **b** Coffee/cappuccino   **c** Mineral water
2 **a** Espresso   **b** Salad   **c** Mineral water
3 **a** Sandwich   **b** Cake   **c** Cup of tea

Grammar: *Can I have …?*

3 **1** help   **2** a   **3** an   **4** Can   **5** have   **6** thank   **7** a   **8** else   **9** please

Vocabulary: prices

4a **1** That's one euro ninety, please.
2 That's two **dollars** forty-five, please.
3 That's fifty **cents**, please.
4 That's six **pounds** twenty-nine, please.
5 That's three **euros** sixty cents, please.
6 That's ninety-nine **cents**, please.
7 That's eleven **euros** forty-nine, please.
8 That's eighty **pence**, please.

4b **1** The CDs are nine pounds eighty-nine.   **2** The pair of shoes is seventy-five euros ninety-nine.   **3** The camera is six euros twenty-nine.   **4** The backpack is twenty-four pounds sixty.   **5** The books are four dollars fifty.   **6** The mobile phone is eighty-nine dollars ninety-nine.

Listening

5 **Food** Chicken sandwich £2.50. Green salad £3.10
Drinks Orange juice £1.20 Mineral water 90p
Coffee Espresso £1.40 Iced coffee £1.95

Lesson 4.2
Vocabulary: clothes and colours

1 **1** brown   **2** white   **3** orange   **4** green   **5** blue   **6** black   **7** yellow   **8** red

2 **1** It's red and white.   **2** It's green, white and red.   **3** It's blue and white.   **4** It's black, red and yellow.   **5** It's red, white and blue.   **6** It's red and yellow.   **7** It's red and white.   **8** It's green, yellow and blue.

3 **1** a hat   **2** a skirt   **3** a coat   **4** a bag   **5** a shirt   **6** a pair of trousers   **7** a pair of shoes   **8** a T-shirt

Grammar: *this, that, these, those*

4 **1** These white shirts are nice.   **2** That white bag is €24.   **3** Is this your suitcase?   **4** Are those tops new?   **5** These shops are closed today.   **6** This is my brother, Clive.   **7** Those bags are beautiful.   **8** How much is that coat?

5 **1** this bag   **2** those shirts   **3** these T-shirts   **4** those tops   **5** this hat   **6** those coats   **7** these skirts   **8** those pairs of trousers

6 **1** How much are those shirts?   **2** How much are these T-shirts?   **3** How much is this hat?   **4** How much are those tops?   **5** How much are those coats?   **6** How much are these skirts?   **7** How much are those pairs of trousers.   **8** How much is this bag?

Reading

7 **1** His surname is Kishore.   **2** He's twenty-four.   **3** He's from Mumbai in India.   **4** His market stall is in Mangaldas Market.   **5** Clothes are on sale.   **6** It's open from Monday to Saturday.   **7** They're 220 rupees.   **8** They're red and pink.   **9** They're 110 rupees.   **10** They're yellow, blue or pink.

Lesson 4.3
Vocabulary: irregular plurals

1 **1** children   **2** women   **3** men   **4** babies   **5** people   **6** wives

Vocabulary: useful phrases

2 **1** Single or return?   **2** pay by credit card?   **3** Sign   **4** or   **5** That's   **6** Can I   **7** PIN number

Grammar: possessive *'s*

3 **1** Julian's car is blue.   **2** Mr Webber's children are two and three years old.   **3** Sally's house is modern.   **4** Petra's parents are from Russia.   **5** Mr Webber's house is small.   **6** Julian's children are twelve and fourteen years old.   **7** Petra's car is green.   **8** Sally's parents are from Poland.   **9** Julian's house is old.   **10** Petra's children are three and six years old.   **11** Sally's car is red.   **12** Julian's parents are from the UK.

4 **1** Is Sally's car blue?   **2** Are Petra's children two and three years old?   **3** Are Julian's parents from the US?   **4** Is Mr Webber's house big?   **5** Are Sally's parents from Russia?   **6** Is Petra's car blue?   **7** Is Julian's house modern?   **8** Are Mr Webber's children twelve and fourteen years old?

5 1 No, they aren't. They're Arabella's shoes. 2 No, it isn't. It's Armand's coffee. 3 No, they aren't. They're Larisa's children. 4 No, it isn't. It's Dimitri's hat. 5 No, they aren't. They're Katarina's books. 6 No, it isn't. It's Giacomo's orange juice.

6 1 I 2 P 3 P 4 I 5 P 6 P 7 I 8 P

Listening

7 Conversation 1 = Picture B   Conversation 2 = Picture A

b **Picture 1** Ticket: to Birmingham. People: one person. Price: £18.10
Picture 2 Film: Red train. People: 1 adult and 1 child. Tickets: £15.50

Review and consolidation
units 3–4

Grammar: The verb *to be*

1 1 are 2 'm/am 3 Are 4 'm not/am not 5 'm/am 6 Are 7 aren't/'re not 8 're/are 9 are 10 're/are 11 Is 12 isn't/'s not 13 's/is 14 Is 15 isn't/'s not 16 are

Possessive adjectives: *my, your, his, its, our, their*

2 1 our 2 His 3 your 4 my 5 Their 6 its 7 her 8 Their

3 1 We aren't teachers. We're students.
2 It's not/isn't ugly. It's beautiful.
3 She's not/isn't from Spain. She's from Italy.
4 Paul and Tom aren't great singers. They're awful singers.
5 I'm not Mrs Campbell. I'm Miss Campbell.
6 Joe's not/isn't in the gallery. He's in the castle.
7 You're not/aren't 23 years old. You're 24 years old.
8 You and I aren't good actors. We're great actors.
9 He's not/isn't from the UK. He's from Australia.
10 It's not/isn't my bag. It's your bag.

Verb *to be*: questions

4 1 A: Are they engineers? B: No, they aren't.
2 A: Is she your sister? B: Yes, she is.
3 A: Am I in room 515? B: No, you're not/aren't.
4 A: Is it your favourite restaurant? B: Yes, it is.
5 A: Are we in your class? B: No, you're not/aren't.
6 A: Is he from Spain? B: Yes, he is.
7 A: Are you Pedro? B: No, I'm not.
8 A: Are Ivan and Vlad brothers? B: Yes, they are.

Can I have … ?; How much … ?

5 1 How much are 2 How much is 3 Can I have a 4 Can I have a 5 How much are 6 How much is 7 Can I have a

This, that, these, those

6 1 This 2 those 3 that 4 this 5 These 6 those 7 that 8 these

Possessive *'s*

7 1 What is Kieran's favourite film? 2 Who is Fiona's sister?
3 Where is Miho's passport? 4 Are they Oliver's shoes?
5 What is Jennifer's email address? 6 Where is Lena's CD?
7 Who is Harvey's manager? 8 Are you Leah's brother?

Vocabulary

8 1 modern 2 Tuesday 3 children 4 street 5 child 6 brother 7 film 8 dollar

9 1 Tuesday 2 dollar 3 film 4 modern 5 Street 6 children 7 brother 8 child

Unit 5 Places

Lesson 5.1
Vocabulary: city, countryside and coast

1a 1 north 2 east 3 south 4 west 5 centre

b 1 buildings 2 beach 3 river 4 mountains 5 trees

2 1 I think this beach is beautiful. 2 I think New York is a great city. 3 I think those buildings are ugly. 4 I don't think Francis is a good manager. 5 I think beautiful countryside is important for a good holiday.

Grammar: *there is/are*

3 1 There's 2 there are 3 There's 4 there's 5 There are 6 there's 7 there are 8 There's 9 There's 10 There are

4 1 There are five small galleries in the west of north of Munsfield. 2 There's an ugly palace in the west of Munsfield. 3 There are four great museums in the south of Munsfield. 4 There are more than eighty good shops in the centre of Munsfield. 5 There's an awful market in the south of Munsfield. 6 There are more than twenty very nice restaurants in the centre of Munsfield. 7 There are three big lakes in the north of Munsfield. 8 There's a beautiful castle in the centre of Munsfield.

Vocabulary: *some, a lot of*

5 1 There are some small galleries in the west of north of Munsfield. 2 There's an ugly palace in the west of Munsfield. 3 There are some great museums in the south of Munsfield. 4 There are a lot of good shops in the centre of Munsfield. 5 There's an awful market in the south of Munsfield. 6 There are a lot of restaurants in the centre of Munsfield. 7 There are some big lakes in the north of Munsfield. 8 There's a beautiful castle in the centre of Munsfield.

6

	Simon Says School of English	Partridge Tree English School	City Centre School of English
City	Cardiff	near Norwich	Glasgow
Where	Wales	the east coast of England	Scotland
Classrooms	14	5	28
Internet café	Yes	Yes (next to the school)	Yes (two)
Big tourist attractions	Cardiff Castle and the Millennium Stadium	Norwich Cathedral and the Inspire Science Centre	the city centre and the lochs

Lesson 5.2
Vocabulary: prepositions of place

1

i	a	g	b	u	r	f	s
n	e	x	t	t	o	d	u
f	x	u	n	l	o	o	n
r	c	o	n	z	a	h	d
o	p	p	o	s	i	t	e
n	m	p	j	s	n	y	r
t	q	n	e	a	r	u	h
o	a	l	k	d	g	m	b
f	d	b	e	h	i	n	d

2 1 in 2 opposite 3 in front of 4 behind 5 under 6 next to 7 near

Vocabulary: nationalities

3 1 Pierre's French. 2 His favourite food is Italian. 3 His car is Japanese. 4 Yu wan's Chinese. 5 Her favourite food is Indian. 6 Her best friend is Scottish. 7 Angela's German. 8 Her favourite food is Russian. 9 Her husband is Brazilian. 10 Telek is Polish. 11 His favourite food is American. 12 His wife is Australian.

Grammar: *There isn't/aren't any; Is/Are there any*

4 1 Is there a chemist? Yes, there is. 2 Are there any banks? No, there aren't. 3 Is there a cinema? No, there isn't. 4 Are there any bookshops? Yes, there are. 5 Are there any newsagents? Yes, there are. 6 Is there a car park? Yes, there is.

5 1 There's a car park. 2 There aren't any galleries. 3 There is a restaurant. 4 There's a supermarket. 5 There aren't any department stores. 6 There isn't a train station. 7 There are two bookshops. 8 There aren't any museums. 9 There isn't a bank. 10 There isn't a cinema.

Listening and reading

6 **1** Is there a hotel near here? **2** Are there any museums or galleries near here? **3** Is there a chemist near here? **4** Are there any cafés or restaurants near here?

7 **a** café **b** hotel **c** restaurant **d** chemist **e** hotel

Lesson 5.3
Vocabulary: abilities

1 **1** dance **2** sing **3** play golf **4** play the piano **5** swim **6** use a computer **7** drive **8** cook

Grammar: *can/can't*

2 **1** I can sing but I can't play the piano. **2** Jim and Jane can cook but they can't drive. **3** Loretta can't swim but she can use a computer. **4** You can't play golf but you can play the piano. **5** Sebastian can cook but he can't dance. **6** You and I can't sing but we can cook.

3 **1** can you **2** I can **3** They can **4** Can you speak **5** can **6** I can't **7** He can **8** Can he

4 **1** Leroy and Lena can use a computer. **2** Jo can't use a computer. **3** No, he can't. **4** Leroy and Lena can't speak Russian. **5** A: Can Jo speak Russian? B: Yes, she can. **6** Simon can use a computer. **7** A: Can Leroy and Lena drive? B: Yes, they can. **8** Jo can't drive. **9** Simon can drive.

Listening

5

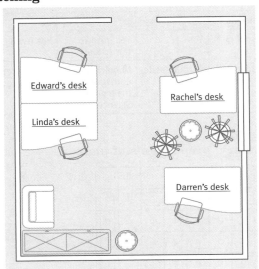

6 **1** She can use a computer. **2** He can speak Italian. **3** She can speak Spanish. **4** She can't speak Russian. **5** She can't speak Italian. **6** He can't speak Russian.

Vocabulary: the time

7 **1** ten o'clock **2** quarter to five **3** half past six **4** ten to ten **5** twenty past eleven **6** one o'clock **7** half past eight **8** quarter past six **9** twenty-five to six **10** five past five

Unit 6 People

Lesson 6.1
Vocabulary: adjectives to describe people

1a **1** short **2** rich **3** old **4** happy **5** thin

b **1** tall – short **2** unhappy – happy **3** fat – thin **4** poor – rich **5** young – old

2 **1** short **2** tall **3** thin **4** fat **5** old **6** young **7** rich **8** poor **9** happy **10** unhappy

Grammar 1: Present Simple (1): *I like*

3a **1** I like cappuccino. **2** I don't like museums. **3** I like rap music. **4** I don't like Arsenal Football Club. **5** I like computers. **6** I don't like Indian food. **7** I don't like espresso. **8** I like children. **9** I like James Bond films. **10** I don't like my manager.

b **1** A: Do you like black coffee? B: Yes, I do. **2** A: Do you like the countryside? B: No, I don't. **3** A: Do you like Chinese food? B: Yes, I do. **4** A: Do you like modern buildings? B: No, I don't. **5** A: Do you like salad? B: Yes, I do. **6** A: Do you like supermarkets? B: No, I don't. **7** A: Do you like department stores? B: Yes, I do. **8** A: Do you like American cars? B: No, I don't. **9** A: Do you like Harry Potter books? B: Yes, I do. **10** A: Do you like The Beatles? B: No, I don't.

Grammar 2: object pronouns

4a **1** them **2** her **3** him **4** it **5** you **6** me

b **1** We **2** us **3** They **4** them **5** She **6** her **7** He **8** him

Reading

5 **1** Do you like British pop music? **2** Who are your favourite actors? **3** Do you like big cities? **4** What are your favourite things in life? **5** Do you like holidays on the coast? **6** What are your favourite things in life?

Lesson 6.2
Vocabulary: jobs and activities

1 **1** Designers **2** Cooks **3** Builders **4** Sales reps **5** Reporters **6** Architects

Grammar 1: Present Simple (2): *we/they*

2 **1** We like our jobs. They don't like their jobs. **2** We work in an office. They don't work in an office. **3** We don't sell cars. They sell cars. **4** We design cars. They don't design cars.

3 **1** do **2** We're **3** do **4** They're **5** like **6** They **7** don't **8** like **9** What **10** you **11** don't **12** like

Grammar 2: *wh-* questions

4a **1** do **2** What **3** do **4** Who **5** Where

b **1** What do you do? **2** Who do you work for? **3** What do you design? **4** Where do you work? **5** Where do you live?

Listening

5a The American man is an accountant. The English man is a businessman.

b **1** can **2** have **3** wife **4** Pardon? **5** go **6** What **7** sell **8** our **9** do **10** accountant

Lesson 6.3
Vocabulary: verbs of routine

1a **1** d **2** c **3** f **4** c **5** a **6** b **7** e

b **1** get up **2** have a shower **3** start work **4** have a sandwich **5** finish work **6** watch TV **7** go to bed

Grammar: Present Simple (3): *he/she/it*

2 **1** She gets up at 10.30. **2** She has a shower at 10.45. **3** She starts work at 11.30. **4** She has a sandwich at 3 o'clock. **5** She finishes work at 5 o'clock. **6** She watches TV at 6 o'clock. **7** She goes to bed at 2.30.

3 **1** He doesn't eat chocolate. **2** She doesn't like chicken. **3** William doesn't start work early. **4** Teresa doesn't get up at seven-thirty. **5** He doesn't go to bed late. **6** She doesn't finish work at five o'clock. **7** He doesn't watch TV every day. **8** Irene doesn't have a new job.

4 **1** Yes, she does. **2** No, she doesn't. **3** Yes, she does. **4** No, she doesn't. **5** Yes, she does. **6** No, she doesn't.

5 **1** I like salad. **2** Cheryl finishes her English class at half past ten. **3** They work in a restaurant. **4** Hilary and Ben don't eat fast food. **5** Connor doesn't eat salad. **6** Do you go to bed early? **7** Does Uma like me? **8** What does she do?

Listening

6

	me	Billy	Bianca	Larry and Mel
me		✓	✓	✓
Billy	✓		✗	✗
Bianca	✓	✗		✓
Larry and Mel	✓	✗	✓	

Writing

7 **1** 89 Gilhurst Road, **2** 2nd December **3** Dear Stephen, **4** How are you? **5** and my team like me. **6** Please write and tell me your news. **7** Best wishes,

Review and consolidation units 5–6

thereis/are; there isn't/aren't; Is/Arethere … ?

1 **1** Is there **2** there is **3** Are there **4** there are **5** There's **6** there's **7** Are there **8** there are **9** There's **10** there are **11** is there **12** there isn't **13** Are there **14** there aren't **15** Is there **16** there is

can/can't

2 **1** Can your daughter drive? **2** Steven can't play the piano. **3** They can speak Spanish. **4** Can you use a computer? **5** Michelle can sing and dance. **6** My husband can't cook.

Present simple

3 **1** cooks **2** don't get up **3** like **4** design **5** doesn't eat **6** eats **7** doesn't like **8** finish **9** write **10** watch **11** loves **12** starts

4 **1** A: Do you play tennis? **B:** Yes, I do.
2 A: Do your sisters like your wife? **B:** No, they don't.
3 A: Does Davina eat a lot? **B:** Yes, she does.
4 A: Do they sell houses? **B:** Yes, they do.
5 A: Does Felix love her? **B:** No, he doesn't.
6 A: Do your friends live in Barcelona? **B:** Yes, they do.
7 A: Does Craig eat fast food? **B:** No, he doesn't.
8 A: Do we have any food in the house? **B:** No, we don't.
9 A: Do you design clothes? **B:** Yes, I do.
10 A: Does Virginia have a brother? **B:** Yes, she does.

Object pronouns: *me, you, him, her, it, us, them*

5 **1** him **2** you **3** them **4** it **5** me **6** her **7** us

Telling the time

6 **1** quarter to four **2** eleven o'clock **3** half past four **4** quarter past five **5** twenty to nine **6** ten past eleven **7** five past nine **8** quarter past one **9** twenty-five to eight **10** half past six

Vocabulary

7 **1** Portuguese **2** Chinese **3** German **4** Italian **5** Indian **6** Polish **7** Spanish **8** Argentine/Argentinian

8 **1** poor **2** young **3** thin **4** short **5** happy

9 **1** f **2** a **3** e **4** h **5** g **6** d **7** b **8** c

Unit 7 Work

Lesson 7.1
Vocabulary: people and places

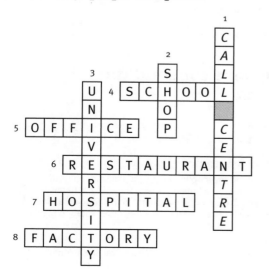

---

2 **1** call centre – call centre worker **2** shop – sales assistant **3** university – lecturer **4** school – teacher **5** office – PA **6** restaurant – waiter **7** hospital – nurse **8** factory – factory worker

Grammar: imperatives

3a **1** Be quiet. **2** Sit down. **3** Don't watch TV. **4** Hold the line. **5** Don't look. **6** Come in.

b **1** Please don't be quiet. **2** Please don't sit down. **3** Please watch TV. **4** Please don't hold the line. **5** Please look. **6** Please don't come in.

How to ... make a business phone call

4 **1** Can I speak to **2** Hold the line, please **3** isn't in his office **4** Hold the line, please. **5** How can I help you? **6** Can I speak to Karen Long **7** It's Ted Baxter. **8** What can I do for you?

Vocabulary: months

5a July 7 October 10 January 1 December 12 August 8 May 5 April 4 February 2 November 11 June 6 September 9 March 3

b **1** April **2** July **3** January **4** August **5** February **6** September **7** December **8** May **9** June **10** October **11** March **12** November

Lesson 7.2
Vocabulary: work phrases

1a **1** call **2** answer **3** write **4** take **5** work **6** work **7** give **8** travel **9** have

b **1** g **2** c **3** d **4** h **5** f **6** e **7** i **8** a **9** b

Grammar: adverbs of frequency

2a **a** always **b** usually **c** often **d** sometimes **e** not often/ not usually **f** never

b **1** I never watch TV in the afternoon. **2** Maggie doesn't usually take work home. **3** We sometimes work outdoors. **4** Do you always go to bed at 11 o'clock. **5** He often plays golf on Sundays. **6** They don't often travel abroad.

3 **1** I don't often swim in the sea. **2** I'm sometimes late for work. **3** I never drive. **4** I usually sing and play the piano at family parties. **5** My manager doesn't usually answer the phone at work. **6** He is always happy on Friday afternoons.

Reading

4a **1** B **2** C **3** A

b **1** Olivia **2** Olivia **3** Darcy **4** Darcy, Olivia **5** Regina **6** Regina, Darcy **7** Darcy **8** Olivia

Writing

5

Hi Jared
Can you call me at home this afternoon? My phone number is 04931 829319.
Thanks,

Dilara

Lesson 7.3
Vocabulary: ordinal numbers and dates
1a

b **1** 21st January   **2** 11th March   **3** 1st May   **4** 12th December
5 20th June   **6** 16th November   **7** 2nd September   **8** 3rd February

Grammar: *would like*

2a **1** What would you like to   **2** I'd like a   **3** Would you like
4 thank you   **5** What would you like   **6** I'd like

b **1** A: Would you like a black coffee? B: No, thank you.   **2** A: What
would you like to eat? B: I'd like a sandwich, please.   **3** A: Would
you like a mineral water? B: No, thank you.   **4** A: Would you like an
orange juice? B: Yes, please.   **5** A: Would you like something to drink? B:
I'd like an espresso, please.   **6** A: Would you like a piece of cake?
B: Yes, please.   **7** A: What would you like to eat? B: I'd like a salad,
please.   **8** A: Would you like an instant coffee? B: No, thank you.

Vocabulary: food

3a **1** vegetables   **2** soup   **3** salad   **4** drinks   **5** fruit
6 desserts   **7** snacks   **8** starters   **9** main course

b **1** starter   **2** soup   **3** snacks   **4** main course   **5** salad
6 vegetables   **7** dessert   **8** fruit   **9** drinks

Listening

4 Conversation 1 = A   Conversation 2 = D   Conversation 3 = F

Unit 8

Vocabulary: leisure activities

1a **1** chess   **2** television   **3** exercise   **4** theatre   **5** cycling
6 eat   **7** tennis   **8** football   **9** walking   **10** reading
11 swimming   **12** sightseeing

b **1** play chess   **2** watch television   **3** do exercise   **4** go to the
theatre   **5** go cycling   **6** eat out   **7** play tennis   **8** play football
9 go for a walk   **10** read a book   **11** go swimming
12 go sightseeing

How to ... talk about things to do

2 **1** You can watch   **2** you can play   **3** you can play   **4** you can do
5 You can go

Grammar: *like + -ing; want + infinitive*

3 **1** want   **2** like   **3** want   **4** like   **5** like   **6** want   **7** like
8 want

4 **1** being   **2** working   **3** finishing   **4** to work   **5** to go
6 working   **7** to be   **8** travelling   **9** selling   **10** to call

Vocabulary: adjectives

5a **1** difficult   **2** easy   **3** boring   **4** fun   **5** exciting
6 interesting

b **1** boring   **2** easy   **3** interesting   **4** difficult   **5** exciting   **6** fun

Writing

6 **1** manorhotel@burbank.net   **2** Manor Bridge Hotel   **3** would like
4 double   **5** 18th and 19th December   **6** How much   **7** included
8 a tennis court   **9** look forward   **10** sincerely

Lesson 8.2
Vocabulary: rooms and furniture

1a **1** sofa   **2** basin   **3** bed   **4** cooker   **5** fridge   **6** coffee table
7 wardrobe   **8** sink   **9** washing machine   **10** armchair   **11** bath
12 car   **13** toilet   **14** mirror
b **Bathroom:** basin, bath, toilet   **Bedroom:** bed, wardrobe, mirror
Kitchen: cooker, fridge, sink, washing machine   **Living room:** sofa,
coffee table, armchair   **Garage:** car

Grammar: *have got/has got*

2a **1** I've got   **2** 's got   **3** hasn't got   **4** 've got   **5** haven't got
6 've got

b **1** She's got   **2** 's got   **3** hasn't got   **4** 's got   **5** hasn't got
6 hasn't got

3 **1** Have, got   **2** have   **3** Have, got   **4** haven't   **5** Has, got
6 has

1 A: Have you got a car? B: Yes, I have.   **2** Ravi's got a new house.
3 My parents haven't got a washing machine.   **4** A: Has your house
got a garage? B: No, it hasn't.   **5** A: Has that hotel got a swimming
pool? B: Yes, it has.   **6** My hotel room hasn't got a bath.   **7** We've
got a new baby.   **8** You've got a beautiful flat.   **9** My sisters haven't
got any children.   **10** A: Have we got any milk in the fridge? B: Yes,
we have.

Listening

5a **1** I've **got** a **new bi**cycle.   **2** Have you **got** a **big** fridge?
3 Mark **hasn't got** my **e**mail ad**dress**.   **4** Have your **friends got**
tele**vis**ions in their **bed**rooms?   **5** They **haven't got** a **cof**fee
table.   **6** She's **got** a **nice so**fa.

Reading

6 **1** No, it isn't.   **2** It's 300 years old.   **3** The main street is Nevsky
Prospect.   **4** His favourite place is St Issak Cathedral.   **5** There are
beautiful paintings and a cashpoint.   **6** They go to their dacha.

Lesson 8.3
How to ... make suggestions

1 **1** How about a game of tennis?   **2** How about/What about
a swim in the lake?   **3** How about/What about that new café
on Cathedral Street?   **4** How about/What about a game of
chess?   **5** How about/What about a film at the cinema?

Grammar: question words

2 **1** What   **2** Who   **3** How   **4** Where   **5** Which   **6** How
7 Who   **8** Which

3 **1** What is her surname?   **2** What does she do?   **3** Where is she
from?   **4** How old is she?   **5** Where does she work?   **6** Who's he?
7 What is the restaurant called?/What is the name of the restaurant?
8 What food does it serve?   **9** Where is it?   **10** How much is a
typical meal?   **11** Who is the owner?   **12** Where is she from?

Vocabulary: food

4

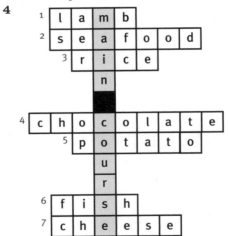

Listening

5a **1** like   **2** How   **3** time   **4** See
6 **1** reservation   **2** table   **3** Come   **4** ready   **5** like   **6** have
7 drink   **8** Still   **9** bill

Review and consolidation
units 7–8

Imperatives

1 **1** c   **2** b   **3** h   **4** f   **5** a   **6** g   **7** e   **8** d

Adverbs of frequency

2 **1** I never turn off my mobile phone.   **2** I'm sometimes late.
3 Do you often work from home?   **4** Are they always happy?
5 I usually have a coffee in the morning.   **6** Do you sometimes play
chess?   **7** She isn't usually early.   **8** They never listen to me.

would like

3 **1** What would you like **to** eat.   **2** Would **you** like a cup of tea?
3 I'd like a coffee, please.   **4** Would **you like** a piece of cake?

like + ing; want + infinitive

4 **1** Adriana likes singing.
2 Does Peter want to go out tonight?
3 My sister doesn't like working from home.
4 Jerome and Kay don't want to go swimming.
5 Alan likes playing golf.
6 Teachers don't usually like checking homework.
7 I don't want to cook tonight.
8 Kiefer wants to meet Julia.
9 Do you like working from home.
10 Do Sheila and Jeff like watching TV.

have got/has got

5 **1** Have (you) got   **2** 've got   **3** Has (it) got   **4** hasn't
5 've got   **6** haven't got   **7** Have (you) got   **8** haven't
9 have got   **10** 've got   **11** Have (they) got   **12** have

question words

6 **1** Where   **2** Who   **3** What   **4** How   **5** Which   **6** What

Dates

7 **1** 14th August   **2** the first of September
3 23rd November   **4** the twenty-second of January
5 11th March   **6** the thirty-first of June
7 8th February   **8** the twelfth of April

Making suggestions

8 **1** What about dinner tomorrow night?
2 How about a game of tennis?
3 What about eating out tonight?
4 How about going cycling?
5 What about playing chess?

Vocabulary

9 **1** h   **2** i   **3** j   **4** g   **5** c   **6** a   **7** d   **8** e   **9** b   **10** f

10 **1** August, February, September
2 call centre worker, nurse, waiter
3 beef, seafood, lamb
4 fun, boring, exciting
5 mirror, wardrobe, sofa
6 go cycling, play football, go to the theatre
7 office, school, hospital

Unit 9 The past

Lesson 9.1
Vocabulary: saying years

1 **1** nineteen eighty-two   **2** two thousand and four   **3** eighteen oh three   **4** nineteen oh nine   **5** nineteen seventy

2a **1** 1st July, 1941   **2** 21st December, 1913   **3** 3rd April, 1973   **4** 28th April, 2001

Grammar: past of to be: affirmative

3 **1** **1** was   **2** were   **3** were   **4** was   **5** was   **6** were
2 **1** were   **2** were   **3** was   **4** were   **5** was   **6** was   **7** were

4 **1** Jeff and I were late for the party.   **2** My son and daughter were at home.   **3** I was a computer engineer.   **4** You were my best friend.   **5** We were in the garage.   **6** Franz was my sister's best friend.   **7** This book was really exciting.   **8** They were at school today.   **9** She was a university lecturer in London.   **10** It was my favourite restaurant.

How to ... talk about childhood

5 **1** When I was young, I was a good actor.   **2** When she was a child, she was beautiful.   **3** When they were children, they were friends.   **4** When he was young, Tim was very thin.   **5** When you were a child, were you happy?   **6** When I was young, I wasn't good at sport.

Vocabulary: prepositions

6 **1** Einstein was born on 14th March, 1879.   **2** Alfred Hitchcock was famous for his films.   **3** Margaret Thatcher was friends with Ronald Reagan.   **4** Martin Luther King and Spike Lee were born in Atlanta in Georgia.   **5** Marilyn Monroe was married to Joe DiMaggio and Arthur Miller.   **6** Lyndon Johnson was President of America from 1963 to 1969.   **7** Some of Nina Simone's music was similar to Billie Holiday's music.   **8** Mikhail Glinka was good at singing/a good singer.

Reading

7 **1** F   **2** T   **3** F   **4** F   **5** F   **6** T

Lesson 9.2
Grammar: past of to be: negatives and questions

1a **1** Cate wasn't born in the UK. She was born in Australia.   **2** Her parents weren't from the UK. They were from the US and Australia.   **3** She wasn't a good singer at school. She was a good actor.   **4** Her subject at university wasn't English. It was Economics.   **5** Her first big film wasn't *Elizabeth*. It was *Oscar and Lucinda*.   **6** Her children weren't born in 2002. They were born in 2001 and 2004.

b **1** Was Cate born in the UK? No, she wasn't.   **2** Were Cate's parents from the UK? No, they weren't.   **3** Was Cate a good singer at school? No, she wasn't.   **4** Was Cate's subject at university English? No, it wasn't.   **5** Was Cate's first big film *Elizabeth*. No, it wasn't.   **6** Were her children born in 2002? No, they weren't.

2 **1** were   **2** were   **3** wasn't   **4** was   **5** was   **6** was   **7** was   **8** were   **9** were   **10** Were   **11** weren't   **12** was   **13** was

3 **1** **Were** you a good singer when you were young?   **2** Richard and Alex **weren't** at work yesterday.   **3** I **wasn't** a maths teacher. I was a science teacher.   **4** **Was** Ronald Reagan a film star?   **5** My father **wasn't** a composer but he was a musician.   **6** **Were** you at home last night?   **7** When **was** your last holiday?   **8** Who **was** your best friend at school?   **9** What **was** Marlon Brando's last film?   **10** **Was** your father a politician?

Vocabulary: yesterday, last, ago

4a **1** C   **2** D   **3** E   **4** A   **5** B

b **1** yesterday evening   **2** a week ago/last week   **3** three years ago   **4** last night   **5** last week   **6** ten days ago   **7** last month   **8** yesterday morning

Listening

5a **1** She wants a job.   **2** It's in Chicago.   **3** She was a sales assistant.   **4** It's a shop in San Diego.   **5** She was a call centre worker.   **6** Yes, she can.

b **1** right   **2** Would   **3** was   **4** wasn't   **5** that   **6** wasn't

Lesson 9.3
Vocabulary: housework

1a **1** cook   **2** do   **3** vacuum   **4** clean   **5** iron   **6** wash

b **A** iron a shirt   **B** clean the bathroom   **C** do the laundry   **D** cook dinner   **E** vacuum the house   **F** wash the dishes

1c **1** Could you iron my shirts?   **2** Could you do the laundry?   **3** Could you cook dinner?   **4** Could you vacuum the house?   **5** Could you wash the dishes?   **6** Could you clean the bathroom?

How to ... ask about an experience

2 **1** How was your flight?   **2** How was school?   **3** How was the party?   **4** How was your weekend?   **5** How was your holiday?

Grammar: Can/Could you ...?; Can/Could I ...?

3 **1** Can I talk to you?   **2** Can you cook dinner?   **3** Could you open the window?   **4** Can I sit down?   **5** Could I work at home tomorrow?   **6** Could you turn on the television?

4 **1** c   **2** b   **3** d   **4** a   **5** e

Writing

5 **1** Long time no see.   **2** How was your holiday?   **3** the weather was very bad   **4** Roza is two years old now.   **5** Last year I was a sales rep.   **6** Could I stay at your house on Wednesday night?   **7** I want to see you.   **8** Could you send me an email

Unit 10 Stories

Lesson 10.1

1a

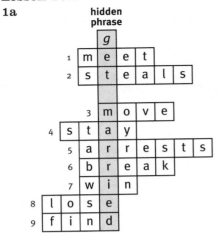

b **1** break your leg **2** get married **3** move to a new house **4** win the lottery **5** a police officer arrests you

Grammar 1: Past Simple: affirmative

2 **1** started **2** cooked **3** walked **4** wanted **5** lived **6** moved **7** played **8** closed **9** listened **10** talked

Pronunciation: /t/, /d/ and /ɪd/

3 **1** wanted /ɪd/ **2** liked /t/ **3** moved /d/ **4** talked /t/ **5** wanted /ɪd/ **6** closed /d/ **7** arrested /ɪd/ **8** listened /d/ **9** asked /t/ **10** finished /t/ **11** played /d/ **12** cooked /t/

Grammar 2: Past Simple: negatives and questions

4a **1** was **2** started **3** didn't move **4** didn't stay **5** moved **6** loved **7** didn't love **8** didn't like **9** didn't stay

b **1** A: Did Van Gogh stay in Paris? B: No, he didn't. **2** A: Did Van Gogh move to London? B: Yes, he did. **3** A: Did Van Gogh love Eugenie Loyer? B: Yes, he did. **4** A: Did Eugenie Loyer love Van Gogh? B: No, she didn't. **5** A: Did Van Gogh like his job? B: No, he didn't.

Listening

5 **1** e **2** f **3** a **4** c **5** d **6** b

Lesson 10.2
Grammar: Past Simple (irregular verbs)

1a **1** got married **2** bought **3** went **4** saw **5** said **6** met **7** gave **8** found

b

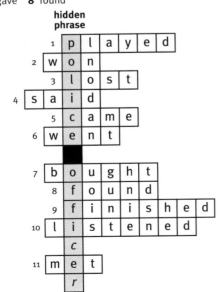

c **1** won **2** got married **3** didn't go **4** said **5** didn't have **6** went **7** looked **8** was **9** bought **10** did he buy **11** didn't buy **12** bought

d **1** Did you find your wallet? **2** Did Terry go out last night? **3** Did they buy a new car? **4** Did you love her? **5** Did Harry move to London? **6** Did you say 'Yes'? **7** Did you lose your passport on holiday? **8** Did we win the lottery?

Vocabulary: high numbers

2 **1** two thousand, one hundred and fifty. **2** one thousand and ten **3** nine hundred and eighty **4** fifteen thousand, six hundred and twelve **5** nine thousand, nine hundred and ninety-nine **6** eighty-six thousand, three hundred and twenty-one **7** one hundred and fifteen thousand, two hundred **8** two hundred thousand, one hundred and nine

Listening

3 **1** 8,850 **2** 190 **3** 770 **4** 6,671 **5** 122 **6** 600 **7** 1,600 **8** 3,000, 8,000 **9** 155 **10** 100,000, 150,000

Writing

4 **1** It was a good week for Cristiano Andrade from Portugal. **2** He got married to Alexandre Serrano on his eighty-first birthday. **3** He met her on holiday in Rio de Janeiro. **4** 'Rio was very beautiful,' he said, 'but Alexandre is very, very beautiful.'

1 It was a bad week for football team Rochdale United. **2** They bought footballer Clive Lightfoot for £1.6 million. **3** Clive arrived at the football club on Monday morning. **4** In the afternoon he broke his leg. **5** Now he can't play football for six months.

Lesson 10.3

Grammar: *going to*

1 **1** They're going to get married. **2** I'm going to move to a hot country. **3** I'm going to go to bed early tonight. **4** She's going to find a new job. **5** We're going to go to the beach this afternoon. **6** You're going to break your leg. **7** He's going to be rich. **8** She's going to cook dinner tonight.

2a **1** I'm going to eat a lot of vegetables. I'm not going to eat meat. **2** He's going to do a lot of exercise. He's not going to surf the Internet every evening. **3** We're going to move house. We're not going to watch a lot of TV. **4** She's going to get a new job. She's not going to go out every night. **5** They're going to travel abroad. They're not going to buy a new car.

b **1** Are you going to eat meat? **2** Is your sister going to get a new job? **3** Are your parents going to buy a new car? **4** Is your husband going to surf the Internet every evening? **5** Where are you and your husband going to move to? **6** What job is your sister going to get? **7** Where are your parents going to travel to? **8** What exercise are you and your husband going to do?

3 **1** What are you going to do next weekend? **2** Are you going to see Jane this evening? **3** Why are they going to learn Spanish? **4** Is he going to hail a taxi? **5** Who's going to wash the dishes? **6** Are we going to eat out tonight? **7** Where are you going to live? **8** What is he going to do?

4a **1** d **2** e **3** b **4** f **5** c **6** a

b **1** He's going to learn to drive. **2** She's going to have a child. **3** He's going to get fit. **4** She's going to go to university. **5** He's going to retire. **6** She's going to start a business.

5a **Name:** Alex Tew **Age:** 21 **Alex's website:** www. milliondollarhomepage.com

b **1** He was poor. **2** He's a university student **3** He bought a website. **4** Each pixel was $1 **5** Alex started the business on 5th August, 2005 **6** Alex made $1,000,000 on 11th January, 2006 **7** Alex plans to finish his university course and start new Internet businesses

Review and consolidation units 9–10

Past of *to be*

1 **1** were **2** was **3** were **4** were **5** was **6** was **7** was **8** Was **9** wasn't **10** was **11** Were **12** weren't **13** was **14** was **15** were **16** weren't

2 **1** Were was he born? **2** What were their names? **3** When were you a teacher? **4** Where was she yesterday? **5** When was your birthday? **6** How was your holiday?

Can I/you; Could I/you

3 **1** you **2** I **3** you **4** I **5** I **6** you **7** I **8** you

Past simple

4 **1** arrested **2** came **3** lost **4** said **5** got **6** played

5 **1 A:** When did the match start? **B:** It started at half past three.
2 A: What did you have for lunch? **B:** I had salad.
3 A: Where did they move to? **B:** They moved to Australia but they didn't move to Sydney.
4 A: Did you go swimming? **B:** We didn't go swimming. We went to the park.
5 A: What did you buy in town? **B:** I bought some clothes.
6 A: Did Marlene take any photos of you. **B:** No, she didn't. But she took some pictures of Michael.
7 A: Where did Harry and Sally meet? **B:** They met at university.
8 A: Where did you see her? **B:** I saw her in a café on Upper Street.

going to

6 **1** Terry's going to get married.
2 I'm not going to live abroad.
3 Samuel's going to learn to dance.
4 Art and Garfunkel aren't going to make a new record.
5 We're going to move to Scotland.
6 The police are going to arrest him.
7 Mike and Danielle are not going to come to the wedding.
8 He's not going to cook dinner.

7 **1** Where are they going to move to?
2 What is he going to buy?
3 Who are you going to talk to?
4 What time/When are you going to meet them?
5 What are they going to play?
6 What is he going to have for dinner?
7 When are you going to retire?
8 What is she going to learn to do?

Vocabulary

8 **1** ten thousand, three hundred and one
2 seven hundred and thirty-three
3 one thousand, one hundred and forty
4 sixty-six thousand
5 one hundred and twelve thousand, five hundred
6 one hundred and one
7 one hundred and ninety-nine thousand, nine hundred and ninety-nine
8 five hundred thousand and five

9 **1** break **2** go **3** have **4** get **5** start **6** win **7** move
8 learn **9** stay **10** get

Pearson Education Limited
Edinburgh Gate
Harlow
Essex CM20 2JE
England
and Associated Companies throughout the world.

www.longman.com

First published 2007
Second impression 2007

Set in 10.5/13pt Meta Plus Book and 10/13pt Meta Plus Normal

Printed in Malaysia,KHL.

ISBN 978-1-4058-2826-0 (book only with key)
ISBN 978-1-4058-2915-1 (book and DVD pack with key)
ISBN 978-1-4058-2827-7 (book for pack with key)

Illustrated by: Beach; F&L Productions; Gary Kaye; Graham Kennedy; Joanne Kerr (New Division); Lucy Truman (New Division); Mark Duffin; Roger Penwill

The publisher would like to thank the following for their kind permission to reproduce their photographs:

(Key: b-bottom; c-centre; l-left; r-right; t-top)

Alamy for pp. 14(2) Blend Images, 15(tr) Jim Powell, 18(C) Douglas Pulsipher, 34(br) Imageshop,49(l) **Art Directors & TRIP**, 66(ml) Imagestate, 66(bl) Ian M Butterfield; Art Directors & TRIP for pp.55, 56(b); **Bananastock** for pp. 13(b), 34(tl); **Bridgeman Art Library** for pp. 67(r) Breton Peasants, 1894 (oil on canvas), Gauguin, Paul (1848-1903) / Lauros / Giraudon, Musee d'Orsay, Paris, France, 67(l) Self Portrait, 1887 (oil on canvas), Gogh, Vincent van (1853-90)/ Musee d'Orsay, Paris, France; **Camera Press** for pp. 9(4), 29(mr); **Courtesy of Canon** for p. 18(B); **Car Photo Library** for p. 18(A); **Corbis** for pp. 14(5) Dann Tardif, 15(cb) Michael Prince,23(tl & bl) Nik Wheeler, 23(1) Jose Fuste Raga, 23(2) Catherine Desjeux, 39(tl) Leland Bobbe, 42 Jim Craigmyle, 61 Bettemenn, 66(tl), Neil Guegan; **Courtesy of New York Museum of Contemporary Art** for p.23(3) Christopher Dawson; **DK Images** for p. 66(br); **Digital Stock** for p. 11(tr); **Digital Vision** for pp. 49(m), 69(t); **Empics** for pp. 9(1), 68; **Eye Ubiquitous** for p. 6(London); **Famous** for p. 14(tr); **Getty Images** for pp. 9(3) Frazer Harrison, 10 Dave Hogan, 14(7) Christian Hoehn, 14(9) Chris Ryan, 15(cr) Butch Martin, 54 Work Book Stock, 57 Wide Group, 60(tr) HultonArchive, 71(b) Daniel Berehulak; **Istock.com** for p. 14(10); **Nature Picture Library** for p. 18(D); **Courtesy of Phillips** for p. 18(F); **Photofusion Picture Library** for p. 14(1); **Photolibrary.com** for p. 41; **Punchstock** for pp. 19(t) Bananastock, 6(Amy) 11(br & bl) 29(tr) 34(tr) Blend Images, 6(Francesca & Calvin) 29(ml) Brand X Pictures, 56(t) Comstock, 6(Sergio) 15(tl) 18(E) 69(b) Corbis, 39(tr) Creatas, 15(c & bl) 49(r) Digital Vision, 34(bl) imageshop, 14(3, 4, 6 &8) 15(l) Imagesource, 15(cl & br) IT Stock, 29(bl) Medio Images, 11(tl) Mike Watson Images, 14(br) Stockbyte, 29(br) Stockdisc, 6(New York) Thinkstock; **Purestock** for p. 53(bl); **Reuters** for p. 66(tr); **Rex Features** for pp. 9(2), 36, 39(br), 62, 71(t); **Stockdisc** for p. 39(m); **Superstock** for pp. 29(tl), 53(r), **TIPS Images** for p. 53(tl); **V & A Images** for p. 60(br), **www.britainonview.com** for p. 33.

Front Cover images by: Punchstock Royalty Free Images: (Digital Vision), (Brand X Pictures)

Picture research by Kevin Brown, cover by Karen Jones and Sandra Hilsdon

Every effort has been made to trace the copyright holders and we apologise in advance for any unintentional omissions. We would be pleased to insert the appropriate acknowledgement in any subsequent edition of this publication.